50 SIMPLE THINGS YOU CAN DO TO SAVE THE EARTH

The EarthWorks Group

NEW ENGLISH LIBRARY
Hodder and Stoughton

CONTENTS

INTRODUCTION TO
THE AMERICAN EDITION

At least once a week, I get a call at NRDC from members and concerned citizens asking what they can do, personally, to combat specific environmental problems. I enjoy that part of the job, helping people to get involved.

So I consult my bookshelf and then point them in a few promising directions. By necessity, the information I give out comes from a diverse array of sources, some easy, some difficult to obtain. No one has ever taken the time to compile it in one place, until now.

The Earth Works Group has given us the solution to this problem in 96 pages – a volume deceptively slim for the amount of information it contains. Want to know the facts about . . . lightbulbs . . . ? It's all here. What can actually be recycled? That's here, too. Even cars, cans, tyres [and garbage] . . . get their moment in the sun.

Like few books in this decade have done, *50 Simple Things* empowers the individual to get up and do something about global environmental problems. No point in letting the news reports and magazine coverage drive you to despair; even the most intractable environmental problems march toward a solution when everyday people get involved.

Few of us can do anything to keep million-barrel oil tankers on course through pristine waters. All of us can do something, every day, to ensure that fewer such tankers are needed. None of us can close the hole in the ozone layer above Antarctica. All of us can help prevent its spread to populated areas by reducing our use of chlorofluorocarbons (CFCs).

Most of the *50 Things* covered here are unbelievably easy. They are the kind of things you would do anyway to save money – if you knew how much you could save. Now you do; the Earth Works Group has done your legwork for you. At the very least, this book shows you how to use energy more intelligently. Don't shiver in the dark, just make sure you're getting as much comfort and convenience as possible from every [pound] you spend on electricity, natural gas, and [petrol].

The 1990s are bringing, I think, a new sense of awareness that institutions alone can never solve the problems that cumulate from the seemingly inconsequential actions of millions of individuals. My [garbage], your use of inefficient cars, someone else's water use – all make the planet less livable for the children of today and tomorrow.

But remember: as much as we are the root of the problem, we are also the genesis of its solution. Go to it!

Chris Calwell,
Energy Program / Atmospheric Protection Initiative
Natural Resources Defense Council (NRDC)

New York, September 1989

INTRODUCTION TO THE UK EDITION

The planet is in deep trouble. Homo sapiens' assault on the air, soil and water life-support systems is reducing our ability to sustain life in its rich and changing diversity. In a dozen years as an environmentalist, my campaigns have moved from the fringes to the political centre stage. Yet the destruction continues. Our challenge is to buck the trends by taking responsiblity for our actions and to force the politicians to do our bidding. *50 Simple Things* tells you how. A publishing phenomenon in the USA, reaching number 1 in *The New York Times* bestseller list and selling over 700,000 copies, this special UK edition deserves to be a similar success. Read it, do it – today!

Stewart Boyle,
Energy and Environment Director
Association for the Conservation of Energy
and author of *The Greenhouse Effect* (NEL, 1989)
London, May 1990

WHAT'S

HAPPENING

THE GREENHOUSE EFFECT

THE GOOD
'The greenhouse effect, when functioning normally, keeps our planet warm. Certain natural gases in the atmosphere . . . form a blanket which allows sunlight to reach the earth's surface, but prevents heat from escaping (much like the glass in a greenhouse). This gas blanket traps heat close to the surface and warms the atmosphere.'

Friends of the Earth

THE BAD
'Now, various industrial gases are thickening the greenhouse blanket . . . trapping more and more heat around the planet . . . [This may create] a temperature rise of 4° to 9°F in the next seven decades. By comparison, the average global temperature has not varied more than 3.6°F in the 18,000 years during which human civilisation has emerged.'

The National Resources Defense Council

THE UGLY
The Greenhouse Gases:
- Carbon Dioxide (CO_2). Responsible for about 50 percent of the greenhouse effect. Every year people add 20 billion tonnes of it to the atmosphere. Main sources of CO_2: burning fossil fuels such as coal, oil, and natural gas, and the destruction of forests, which release CO_2 when they are burned or cut down.

- Chlorofluorocarbons (CFCs). Responsible for 15 to 20 percent, and also destroy the earth's ozone layer.

- Methane. 18 percent. Produced by cattle, rice fields, gas leaks and by landfills.

- Nitrous Oxide. 10 percent. Formed by burning fossil fuels, microbes, and the breakdown of chemical fertilisers.

- Ozone. Comes from ground-based pollution caused by motor vehicles, power plants, oil refineries.

'Nobody made a greater mistake than he who did nothing because he could only do a little'.

Edmund Burke

AIR POLLUTION

WHAT IS IT?

'Ozone, the primary component of smog, is a gas formed when nitrogen oxide and hydrocarbons combine in sunlight. In the atmosphere, ozone occurs naturally as a thin layer that protects us from the sun's ultraviolet rays. But when it is formed at ground level it is deadly.'

The Clean Air Project

WHO DOES IT AFFECT?

'One in five people in the UK are potentially at risk from air pollution, especially the old, children under two and those with respiratory illnesses.'

Friends of the Earth

'Most people don't realise that smog harms other forms of life as well as people. Ozone smog is responsible for extensive damage to [trees] . . . It's also to blame for crop losses.'

The Clean Air Project

WHERE DOES IT COME FROM?

'Cars, trucks, and buses . . . are one of the chief sources of ozone. In 1986, [in the US] 6.5 million tons of hydrocarbons and 8.5 million tons of nitrogen oxide were [spewed] into the air by motor vehicles . . . Utilities, oil, and chemical plants, are also a large part of the problem, accounting for approximately half the hydrocarbon emissions and half the nitrogen oxide emissions in the US.'

The Public Interest Research Groups

Natural alternatives: mineral oil works well as a lubricant on door hinges.

OZONE DEPLETION

UP, UP . . .
'High above our heads, a fragile, invisible layer of ozone shields the earth's surface against dangerous solar ultraviolet radiation. The ozone layer has been there for eons.'

The Natural Resources Defense Council

. . . AND AWAY
'But now man is destroying this protective shield. Chlorofluorocarbons (CFCs), halons, and other manmade chemicals are wafting up to the stratosphere, 6 to 30 miles overhead. There they break down, releasing . . . atoms that destroy ozone.'

The Natural Resources Defense Council

WHAT ARE CFCs?
'CFCs are put to hundreds of uses because they are relatively non-toxic, nonflammable, and do not decompose [easily] . . . Because they are so stable, they will last for up to 150 years. The CFC gases rise slowly to about 25 miles where the tremendous force of the sun's ultraviolet radiation shatters the CFC, freeing the chemical element chlorine. Once freed, a single atom of chlorine destroys about 100,000 molecules of ozone before settling to the earth's surface years later. 3 percent, and perhaps up to 5 percent, of the global ozone layer has already been destroyed by CFCs.'

***International Wildlife* magazine**

WHAT NEXT?
'As ozone diminishes in the upper atmosphere, the earth receives more ultraviolet radiation, which promotes skin cancers and cataracts, and depresses the human immune system . . . As more ultraviolet radiation penetrates the atmosphere, it will worsen these health effects, reduce crop yields and fish populations. It will affect the well-being of every person on the planet.'

The Worldwatch Institute

Just a 1 percent reduction in atmospheric ozone could result in 15,000 new cases of skin cancer in the US alone.

HAZARDOUS WASTE

GROWING CONCERN
'In 1983, 266 million tons of hazardous waste were generated [in America] – more than a ton for every person in the United States.'
Environmental Action Foundation

GET RID OF THEM?
'There is no safe way of disposing of [hazardous] wastes once they are produced. Current methods of disposal are landfill, chemical treatment, and incineration. Through all these methods pollutants are dispersed into the environment.'
Greenpeace

HASTE MAKES WASTE
'Chemicals have become an indispensable part of our daily lives. We enjoy the convenience of such chemically-derived products as plastics, detergents, and aerosols, and yet we are often unaware of the hidden price tag associated with them. Eventually they find their way into water and/or the ground via landfills, drains, or sewage sludge.'
The Clean Water Action Project

WASTE NOT . . .
'Advanced nations manufacture some 70,000 different chemicals, most of which have not been thoroughly tested . . . Careless use and disposal of these substances contaminate our food, water, and air, and seriously threaten . . . the ecosystems on which we depend.'
Coalition for a Global Tomorrow

. . . WANT NOT
'The potential for waste reduction is enormous. The Congressional Office of Technology Assessment in the USA has stated that a 50 percent reduction of hazardous wastes over five years is feasible.'
Greenpeace

In Britain 1 million cars are scrapped each year.

ACID RAIN

HOW DO WE GET IT?

'Sulphur and nitrogen oxides, pollutants released by coalburning electric-power plants or motor vehicles, are spewed into the atmosphere. There they are changed chemically . . . and they fall back to earth as acidified rain or snow. This destroys plant and animal life in streams, damages forests, and even erodes buildings.'

Cleaning Up the Outdoors

HOW BAD IS BRITAIN?

Britain is the largest producer and exporter of the components of acid rain in Western Europe, generating 3.7 million tonnes of sulphur dioxide (65 percent from power stations in 1986) and 1.9 million tonnes of nitrogen oxides (40 percent from power generation and 40 percent from traffic).

'By 1993, if present trends continue, Britain should have achieved a 30 percent reduction in sulphur dioxide emissions. But it could still be producing as much sulphur dioxide as France, West Germany, Sweden, Denmark, Norway, Austria, Switzerland, Luxembourg and the Netherlands put together.'

The Green Consumer Guide by John Elkington and Julia Hailes

WHAT CAN BE DONE?

'It is estimated that to restore our environment to its natural, pre-industrialised state, we would have to reduce sulphur emissions by 90 percent and nitrogen oxide emissions by 70 to 75 percent. The technology exists to do this.'

Greenpeace

Each day, 300 million gallons of sewage is pumped into Britain's seas, most of it untreated or partially filtered.

VANISHING WILDLIFE

URBAN SPRAWL
'In 1980 there were 4.4 billion people on earth. In 1990, there will be 5.2 billion. Every day, some of these human beings move into places on the planet where only plants and animals used to live. Forests are cut down. Wetlands, oceans, ice caps, and prairies are invaded.'
World Wildlife Fund, US

GOING . . .
'There are between 5 and 30 million species on earth. Only 1.4 million have been given names. A third of all species could become extinct by the year 2050.'
World Wide Fund for Nature

GOING . . .
The International Union for Conservation of Nature and Natural Resources has data on nearly 6,000 species of mammals, birds, reptiles, amphibians, fish, insects and invertebrates which are in danger, and 578 more are considered vulnerable if present trends continue. In addition, some 25,000 species of flowering plants are considered to be threatened.

. . . GONE
'Nearly all of Africa's elephants will be gone in 20 years if the present killing rate continues.'
Defenders **magazine**

EQUAL PROTECTION
'Only a few popular and charismatic mammals are receiving adequate concern and protection . . . It is important to fight also for less well-known species . . . particularly insects, fish, amphibians, reptiles and plants. Otherwise, we will be allowing crucial pieces of the fabric that holds ecosystems together to disappear.'
The Ecology Center Newsletter

In the last 3 decades 85% of the world's rhinos have been killed for their horn.

GROUNDWATER POLLUTION

WATER, WATER, EVERY WHERE?

'97 percent of the earth's [water] supply is contained in our oceans, and 2 percent is frozen. We get our water from the 1 percent that is left, which comes from one of two places: the earth's surface (rivers, lakes and streams) or from . . . groundwater.'

The National Coalition Against Pesticide Use

WHERE DOES IT COME FROM?

'Groundwater . . . is water that fills the cracks and pore spaces in rocks and sediments . . . beneath the surface of the earth. Most groundwater is naturally pure . . . In many cases, groundwater remains undisturbed for years, even centuries, before it is used . . . More than 90 percent of the world's total supply of drinkable water is groundwater.'

The Water Pollution Control Federation

THE PROBLEM

'[Petrol] or other harmful liquids have been allowed to leak from underground storage tanks into the groundwater supply. Pollutants seep . . . from poorly constructed landfills or septic systems. Groundwater [is] polluted by runoff from fertilised fields [and] industrial areas. Homeowners contribute to groundwater contamination by dumping household chemicals down the drain or . . . on the ground.'

The Water Pollution Control Federation

'The gloomy conclusions of "The Groundwater Nitrate Problem" – a British Geological Survey report – are that unless agricultural land-use practices change, the EEC 50mg/litre limit will eventually be almost universally breached.'

HDRA *1990 Organic Gardening Catalogue*

continued

Using a broom, not a hose, to clean pavements and steps saves hundreds of gallons of water.

ALL THAT GARBAGE

WHERE DOES IT GO?
'About 18 million tons of rubbish – 90 percent of the rubbish we produce – are chucked into landfill sites every year. About 60 percent of this is packaging. It costs £700 million to dump this rubbish, in 5,000 landfill sites. The Department of Trade and Industry estimate that 60 percent (in weight) consists of recyclable materials.'
Waste Watch

We are currently excavating more potential landfill sites than we are filling, but, according to Friends of the Earth, we are running out of appropriate sites.

FLOATING GARBAGE
'No one really knows how much plastic is fouling up the oceans. But a recent report estimated that up to 350 million pounds of packaging and fishing gear alone may be lost or dumped by fishermen and sailors each year. Millions of pounds more may come from individuals, private boats, and factories.'
***International Wildlife*
magazine**

COMMON SENSE
'The cheapest and safest ways to deal with [rubbish] are those that make common sense: producing less waste and recycling more.'
The Environmental Defense Fund

KEEP BRITAIN TIDY
'There is a correlation between picking up the litter outside your door and the Brazilian rainforests. Litter is a personal responsibility: it's you and me who drop the litter, not the local council. This responsibility is every bit as important as looking after the sick and underprivileged in our society.'
The Tidy Britain Group

Don't leave puddles of antifreeze on the ground – pets like the sweet taste of the toxic.

SAVING ENERGY AND WATER, SAVING THE EARTH

After living through the 1970s, we are all familiar with the sensible home economics of saving energy. For example, the insulation argument goes: if we insulate our homes, we will keep OPEC at bay. We will also save so much money on utility bills that we will recoup our investments in a year or two and pocket the difference from then on. This is not a bad argument.

But it does not take the environment into account. As a result, many people have no idea whether saving energy, or water, makes an ecological difference. Will a squeeze of sealant around your draughty windows really have any effect on our shattered environment? The answer is a resounding yes.

● If you burn less oil, coal or wood, there will be less carbon dioxide and other greenhouse gases emitted into the atmosphere, and global warming will be slowed.

● If less coal needs to be burned at an electric power plant, there will be less acid rain, less strip mining, and less air pollution.

● If less electricity is needed, there will be less nuclear waste, less uranium tailings left exposed at mines, less power plants to be built, and less chance of future Chernobyls.

● Less petrol burned means less smog and greenhouse gases.

● Less oil extracted from the earth means less disruption of wildlife for drilling, less offshore oil drilling, and less chance of disastrous oil spills.

Similarly, saving water is not just something to do in a drought, when the resource is scarce. Every drop of water wasted is a drop less of a wild and scenic river, a drop less of a salmon run, a drop more in a glorious waterfall.

Every year the average Briton uses 10,000 gallons of water, 500% more than the average Indian.

Water conservation also reduces the amount of chemicals and energy used in water treatment and sewage treatment. It reduces the amount of energy needed to pump the water to your home or heat the water once it is there. Since water heating is generally the second largest energy user in the home, there are large savings to be made here.

In terms of what you can do to save the earth, small savings are certainly beautiful, too. The Herculean task of shifting our lifestyles back into balance with the earth is no longer overwhelming when broken down into the manageable pieces of influence each of us has in our personal lives. The compact fluorescent light bulb and the energy-efficient appliance represent conscious, and valuable, efforts to reduce the impact that human beings will have on the world. And, in fact, the small changes we have made in the last fifteen years have already had a considerable impact on the energy we consume.

Conservation, then, does not mean 'freezing in the dark,' as Ronald Reagan once said. Conservation can be accomplished by simple, cost-effective measures that require little change in lifestyle. For people concerned with saving the earth, that is good news indeed.

1,000 tonnes of paper are put in our dustbins each week. Less than 5 percent is recycled.
Karina Lutz, Managing Editor, *Home Energy* **magazine**

We put 1000 tonnes of paper into our dustbins each week.

SIMPLE

THINGS

1. REDUCE JUNK MAIL

BACKGROUND. We do not usually think of junk mail as an environmental problem, just a nuisance. But the unwanted paper we receive through our letter boxes every year accounts for millions of wasted trees.

DID YOU KNOW

● Because of the way it is distributed, no one really knows how much true junk mail – i.e. mail that is addressed to The Occupier, or that is not addressed at all – we get.

● Professionally targeted direct mail is now beginning to take off in this country, each person receiving 29 pieces per annum. Americans receive an average of 300 pieces.

● In 1989, 2,117 million items of direct mail were issued, an estimated 70,000 tonnes. The average household in Britain was sent 1½ items per week – 32 percent business, and 68 percent consumer mail.

● Junk mail is made possible by Royal Mail policies that enable bulk mailers to send material at reduced rates.

SIMPLE THINGS TO DO

● It is possible to have your name removed from direct mailing lists by writing to the Mailing Preference Service, Freepost 22, London W1E 7EZ. This service claims to be able to stop those companies who already have your name from continuing to send you circulars.

● As for the others, if you ask the companies concerned to stop the barrage, they are obliged to do so, by law.

● Recycle the junk mail you already get. If it is printed on newsprint, throw it in with the newspapers. If it is quality paper, make a separate pile for it. Self-sealed envelopes and those with plastic windows cannot be recycled. Gummed envelopes are fine.

Over a third of British household rubbish is made up of packaging.

2. SNIP FOUR-PACK AND SIX-PACK RINGS

BACKGROUND. Plastic four- and six-pack holders – the rings used to bind canned beer, soft drinks, oil, etc. – have become a hazard to birds and other marine life.

How do they get into the water? They are left on beaches and wash into the sea, or they are dumped into our rivers with tonnes of other garbage, and gradually make their way into the sea; or they are dumped into seaside landfills, and erosion or wind propels them into the water. Once they are floating in the sea, they are potential hazards to marine life.

DID YOU KNOW?

● These plastic holders are virtually invisible underwater, so marine animals cannot avoid them.

● Gulls and terns – birds that frequent recreational areas and dumps near the sea – sometimes catch one loop around their necks while fishing. Then another loop gets hooked on a stationary object. Result: they drown or strangle themselves.

● Many birds catch fish by plunging into the water. Occasionally, one will dive straight into a four- or six-pack ring. Result: the bird ends up with the ring stuck around its bill, and unable to open its mouth, it starves to death.

● Young seals and sea lions get the rings caught around their necks. As they grow, the rings get tighter and the animals suffocate.

SIMPLE THINGS TO DO

● Before you throw plastic ring holders into the garbage, snip each circle with a pair of scissors.

● When you are on the beach, or by a river or lake, pick up any four- or six-pack rings you find and take them with you. Snip them before you throw them away.

Annually, the US produces the equivalent of 10 lbs of plastic for every person on earth.

3. USE A CLEAN DETERGENT OR WASHING POWDER

BACKGROUND. Phosphates, chemical compounds containing phosphorus, are found in most detergents, washing powders and liquids. They soften water and prevent dirt particles from being redeposited on clothes.

Unfortunately, there are severe ecological side-effects. As phosphates empty into rivers and lakes they cause algae bloom – i.e. they fertilise algae to the point where it grows out of control. When, in its natural cycle, algae dies, the bacteria that cause it to decay – a process requiring huge amounts of oxygen – use up the oxygen needed by other plants and marine life to survive. Result: lakes and streams can die.

DETERGENT DATA

● Up to 30 percent of most washing powders are made up of phosphates.

● More than 25 percent of the phosphate in our fresh water has been contributed to by detergents.

● Other components of detergents include enzymes, which can cause allergic skin reactions; and bleaches, fluorescers and perfumes, which are not quick to biodegrade.

SIMPLE THINGS TO DO

● Use a little less detergent. Manufacturers tend to recommend more detergent than necessary.

● Use a phosphate-free detergent. Ecover products, which are now widely available at supermarkets, are designed to biodegrade within 5 days.

● If your washing powder or liquid claims to be 'biological', it means that it contains enzymes. You should avoid enzymes if you have sensitive skin.

99.5% of all the fresh water on earth is in icecaps and glaciers.

4. ECOLOGY IN THE KITCHEN

BACKGROUND. The kitchen is a good place to start integrating an environmental consciousness into your everyday life. By using environmentally sound kitchen products instead of unsound ones, you can help conserve resources and play a part in changing our habits. Some alternative products may cost more because, at the moment, the demand is low. But as more of us buy them, prices will drop.

DID YOU KNOW
● Your coffee filters, paper towels etc. are white because they are bleached. But this is not a benign aesthetic: the process of bleaching paper is responsible for creating dioxin, a deadly toxic which is dumped into our rivers.

● In many cases, paper is bleached despite the fact we rarely look at it. We buy, for example, millions of bleached coffee filters every year, and then throw them away after using them once.

● To make plastic cling wrap, manufacturers add 'plasticisers', potentially harmful chemicals that can work their way into your food.

SIMPLE THINGS TO DO
● Use reusable containers to store food in your fridge instead of habitually wrapping food in aluminium foil or clingfilm.

● Use unbleached coffee filters. They are available in a number of chain supermarkets in the UK. Another alternative is to use cotton coffee filters.

● Keep rags in the kitchen to wipe up spills instead of using paper towels every time. Then wash and reuse them.

● Instead of foil or plastic cling wrap, use re-usable plastic boxes for your sandwiches etc.

About 73% of Britain's paper is thrown away without thought of recycling.

5. GETTING INTO HOT WATER

BACKGROUND. You probably do not pay too much attention to your hot water tank – it just sits in a dark corner gathering cobwebs. But maybe you should. After all it is the second-largest energy-user in the British home.

DID YOU KNOW

● Heating water accounts for about 20 percent of the money we spend on energy in our homes.

● The temperature of your boiler can be controlled by a water cylinder thermostat. Not all boilers will necessarily have one, but they can be easily fitted.

● To set your boiler at less than 60°C may pose a health risk: bacteria that cause Legionnaire's Disease can live at high temperatures.

● Over 3 million British homes have boilers that are more than 10 years old.

SIMPLE THINGS TO DO

● The most important thing is to insulate your hot water tank. If there was no jacket before, you could save 7 to 8 percent of the energy you have been using – in cash terms that is between £40 and £80 a year.

● By replacing your boiler and fitting up-to-date controls, you may save as much as 35 percent on your fuel bills.

● The Energy Efficiency Office recommend that people should keep the temperature at 60°C, so if your boiler is set higher, turn it down.

A trigger nozzle on your hose will save at least 15 gallons when you wash your car.

6. MAKE A PHONE CALL

BACKGROUND. This may be cheating a little bit, because it does not affect the environment directly, but when you start on a project as important as this, it is essential to know what assistance is available. After all, there is not much use in getting people excited about saving cans and bottles for recycling, if they do not know where to take them.

So we suggest that you do a little research on your own. Familiarise yourself with some of the subjects dealt with in this book and enquire about them locally. You may be surprised at the diversity of services available.

Call your local electricity board:
● Check on the availability of energy audits.
● Ask about free information (literature on how to save electricity etc.).

Call your regional water board:
● Check to see what conservation devices, services or information they offer.

Call your local recycling centre:
● How do you find it? Look it up in the Yellow Pages or ask your local council for assistance in locating your nearest centre.
● Ask what materials they do collect and if there are any glaring omissions, request that they set up schemes for them.

Flick through the Yellow Pages and see what is listed under:
● Recycling
● Environmental agencies
● Heating services
● Plumbing/Electrical Supplies etc.

It is reckoned by government officials that as much as 60% of Britain's household rubbish could be reclaimed.

7. BRUSH UP ON PAINT

BACKGROUND. Everyone faces a painting decision sometime. The decision should be more than just what colour, though. What kind of paint you use, and what you do with it once you have finished, has a direct impact on the environment. In fact, even cleaning your paint brushes has an effect.

DID YOU KNOW

• Pigment in oil-based paint is often made with heavy metals like cadmium and titanium dioxide.

• Not only is oil-based paint toxic, but the by-products of manufacturing it are also nasty pollutants. When titanium dioxide is used, for example, liquid waste containing sulphuric acid, heavy metals and chlorinated hydrocarbons is generated.

• Disposing of any paint by pouring it onto the ground is risking groundwater contamination.

SIMPLE THINGS TO DO

• Use emulsion paint, which is water-based, wherever possible. Emulsion for both interior and exterior decoration is widely available.

• Remember, most old paints contain lead, which is extremely toxic. So when rubbing down old walls for redecoration, use wet sandpaper, and keep children out of the way.

• Most paints are now generally lead-free, but a number with lead content are still available to the trade. Avoid these.

• Clean paint brushes safely. Don't wash them outside – the brush cleaner will threaten the groundwater.

• Letting any oil-based paint products evaporate pollutes the atmosphere, so keep the lids on tight.

• Set up a community paint exchange. Why let your left-over paint go to waste, when someone else could use it?

• Donate unused paint to a school or hospital.

The biggest domestic water consumer is the toilet – 2.2 gallons for every flush.

8. TIME TO RE-TYRE?

BACKGROUND. Tyres have a bigger impact on the environment than you might think. By maintaining them properly, you help conserve the energy and resources that would go into making new ones, prevent the pollution generated by tyre production, save petrol, and reduce the problems created when they are thrown away. For tyres are bulky, do not decompose, and provide places for mosquitoes to breed.

TYRE TRIVIA

● Every year over 30 million car and lorry tyres, weighing 218,000 tonnes, wear out in Britain; in the US some 240 to 260 million tyres are discarded.

● About 50 percent of Britain's scrap tyres are simply buried in landfills, while Japan landfills only 1 percent and West Germany 11 percent.

● It takes half a barrel of crude oil to produce the rubber in one lorry tyre.

THE COST OF INFLATION

● We do not normally think of tyre inflation as an environmental issue, but it is. Keeping tyres properly inflated preserves the life of the tyres, preventing premature wear from overflexing and overheating. It also saves petrol.

● Underinflation can waste up to 5 percent of a car's fuel by increasing rolling resistance. This means it will add 5 percent more carbon dioxide, nitrogen oxides and smog-causing hydrocarbons to the atmosphere.

THE RADIAL DIFFERENCE

● Radial tyres really do improve petrol mileage. Steel-belted tyres are generally the most efficient.

● If all cars in the US were equipped with the most efficient tyres possible, the fuel savings would equal 400,000 barrels of oil per day.

Annually, 3.5 million medical tests are still administered on live animals.

RECYCLING TYRES

● Tyre recycling is still a fairly untapped area. But it is a promising one. The energy used to produce a pound of virgin rubber is 15,700 BTUs (British Thermal Units). Producing one pound of recycled rubber requires only 4,600 BTUs, a saving of 71 percent.

● Recycled rubber can be used for tyres, adhesives, wire and pipe insulation, brake linings, conveyor belts, carpet padding, lawn mower and tractor tyres, hoses, sporting goods, and many other products.

● Ground rubber 'crumbs' can be added to asphalt for paving roads, runways, playgrounds and running tracks. Rubber added to asphalt will increase pavement life by 4 to 5 times, and reduce the amount of resurfacing materials required.

● It is estimated that some 35 percent of car tyres and 60 percent of lorry tyres are suitable for recycling, but Britain is only recycling 14 percent of car tyres and 27 percent of lorry tyres, and the situation is deteriorating.

SIMPLE THINGS TO DO

● Buy the longest-lasting, most fuel-efficient tyres possible. Ask your tyre dealer about the rolling resistance and the mileage performance of the tyres you are considering.

● Make sure your tyres are properly inflated, the wheels balanced and (every 6 to 8,000 miles) rotated.

● If you have a choice between tyre dealers offering roughly equal prices, patronise the one who gets his tyres recycled. At least ask what they do with old tyres. If they are not recycled, check if there is a tyre recycling centre in your area and take them there.

● Support regional and national efforts to recycle tyres, to use more recycled rubber in tyres, and to convert discarded tyres into energy. Help lobby the government by writing to your MP.

When you buy new appliances, go for the most energy-efficient models.

9. ENERGY AT HOME

BACKGROUND. Energy specialists repeatedly stress that we can have a significant impact on the environment simply by properly maintaining major appliances like fridges, ovens, washing machines etc.

Here are a few examples of the simple ways you can save with your appliances.

DID YOU KNOW

● We use energy much more efficiently than we did 20 years ago. For example, it now takes 80 percent less energy to heat the average home's water than it would have done in 1970. Most savings, however, are due to better insulation, not less use of energy. Often these improvements are offset by the growing number of appliances in our homes.

● Statistics show that overall there has been a 2 percent rise in our energy consumption in the home since 1970.

OVEN TIPS

● If you are buying a gas cooker, ensure it has an electric ignition system. If your cooker relies on a pilot light, turn it off and use matches.

● If you are buying an electric cooker, remember that they cost about three times as much to run as gas cookers. Electric grills are particularly inefficient.

● Microwave ovens use only a third to half as much energy as conventional ovens.

FRIDGE TIPS

● If your fridge and freezer are 5°C colder than necessary, their energy consumption will increase by up to 25 percent. Check their temperatures. For fridges and freezers temperatures are laid down by international standards. Your fridge should be +5°C; 0°C for fish and meat compartments. Your freezer should be −6°C (one star), −12°C (two star) and −18°C (three and four star).

Don't forget, aluminium foil is recyclable.

- For efficient operation, clean the condenser coils on the back or bottom of your fridge at least once a year.
- Keep the door gasket clean to make sure the seal is not being broken by dried-on food.

WASHING MACHINE, DRYER AND DISHWASHER TIPS

- About 12 percent of household water is used in washing machines and dishwashers. You will save a lot of water if you wait until you have a full load to wash.
- Up to 90 percent of the energy used for washing clothes goes on heating the water. A warm water wash and a cold rinse will work just as well as a hot water wash and a warm rinse on nearly all clothes. The temperature of the rinse does not effect the cleaning.
- Clean your dryer's lint trap after every load to keep the air circulating efficiently.

For more information on energy conservation in your home, why not pop into your local electricity or gas board showroom – it may save you a lot of money.

A pine cone stuffed with peanut butter is a good way to feed birds during the winter.

10. DON'T GO
WITH THE FLOW

BACKGROUND. Each of us uses around 28 gallons of water every day, while the average British family of four consumes about 770 gallons per week. A household can save thousands of gallons of water each year by getting a grip on its taps.

DID YOU KNOW
• A running tap probably uses a lot more water than you think – it puts over 2 gallons of water down the drain every minute it is on.

• You can easily use 6 to 12 gallons of water if you leave the tap running while you brush your teeth.

• Washing dishes with the tap running can use an average of 20 gallons of water.

• If you shave with the water on, you use an estimated 6 to 14 gallons each time.

• If you wash your car at home, using a hose, you can use up to 100 gallons of water.

SIMPLE THINGS TO DO
• Brushing your teeth. If you just wet and rinse your brush, you use only half a gallon of water. Savings: up to 9 gallons each time you brush.

• Shaving. If you fill the basin, you will only use around 1 gallon of water. Savings: up to 13 gallons each time you shave.

• Washing dishes (by hand): if you fill a sink, you use about 4 gallons of water. Savings: up to 16 gallons each time you wash dishes.

• Washing your car. If you use a sponge and a bucket, you use around 15 gallons. Savings: over 80 gallons of water.

The average British man will spend about 20 weeks of his life shaving.

11. ECOLOGY AT THE PETROL STATION

BACKGROUND. The type of petrol we choose has an impact on the environment.

Leaded petrol is an environmental hazard. Airborne lead from vehicle exhaust causes liver, kidney and brain damage in humans. Scientists suspect that it is responsible for damaging crops as well. Motor vehicles in Britain are responsible for the release of over 2,500 tonnes of lead into the air.

DID YOU KNOW

- 90 percent of petrol stations in the UK are now supplying unleaded fuel, but only 27 percent of drivers are using it.
- All Honda cars imported into the UK since 1972 have been able to run on unleaded petrol.

SIMPLE THINGS TO DO

- If you have not already changed to unleaded petrol, find out whether your car can take it. Some cars can run on either leaded or unleaded, others need to be converted.
- Buying a new car? Check that it runs on unleaded petrol.
- Enquire about your firm's policy on unleaded cars. If it does not insist that all new company cars should run on unleaded petrol, ask why not.
- Butane, a component of petrol, helps create ozone smog when it evaporates. So when you fill your petrol tank, the escaping vapours are polluting the atmosphere. In the US plastic hoods have been introduced on many petrol pump nozzles to control these vapours. The special petrol hose fits over the tank opening and sucks fumes into the underground storage tank, preventing the vapours from escaping. More and more states are requiring petrol stations to install such equipment. There seem to be no plans to repeat the exercise in Britain. Ask your regular petrol station what their company is doing to fight the escape of butane, or write to your MP to express your concern.

Remember you can wash out plastic bags and reuse them.

12. THE TWILIGHT OZONE

BACKGROUND. Rectifying ozone depletion (see p10) is one of the greatest challenges we face. The problem is immediate and severe, but it is not out of control yet. The ozone layer is still there, and we can save it.

Constructive action begins with an understanding of what is causing the depletion, and what each of us can do about it.

DID YOU KNOW

● The ozone layer is being depleted by manmade gases (chlorofluorocarbons – also called CFCs – and halons) that are found in homes and offices all over the world.

● At one time, CFCs were considered harmless. So manufacturers used them in many different products.

● They are still being used today. Freon, used as a coolant in fridges, is a CFC.

● Some types of polystyrene foam, which is often referred to as 'styrofoam', are still made with CFCs. Contrary to what you might assume, CFCs are not just released in the manufacturing process, they are also released into the atmosphere as the foam breaks or crumbles.

● Until very recently, CFCs were commonly used as propellants in aerosol cans. Of the 800 million manufactured in the UK in 1987, 80 percent contained CFCs. By the end of 1989 over 85 percent were CFC-free.

● However, asthma medication sprays, and video recorder and sewing machine cleaning sprays still use CFCs as propellants. And the world's silliest use of CFCs – canned confetti.

● Some fire extinguishers sold for the home use halons as propellants. Unfortunately, these halons will eventually attack the ozone layer, even if the fire extinguishers are never used, because the ozone-depleting gases gradually leak into the atmosphere.

A fraction of 1% of drinkable tap water is actually drunk.

SIMPLE THINGS TO DO

● Do not buy halon fire extinguishers.

● Avoid polystyrene foam (see p42). This includes form-fitting packing materials – those that protect electronics in boxes, for instance – and foam worms. If you cannot tell whether the foam was made with CFCs, ask. Eventually retailers will pass on your concern to manufacturers.

● If you are planning to use hard foam insulation, make sure there are no CFCs in it. Non-CFC foam insulation is available. It is nearly as effective, and will not make a hole in the sky. Look at fibreglass and cellulose insulation too.

● Do not buy aerosol cans containing CFCs, or better still, do not use aerosols at all. Even with substitute gases, aerosol sprays are not benign: propane and butane, the hydrocarbons used as propellants in most aerosols today, help create smog when they interact with sunlight. Lots of products come with non-aerosol vacuum pumps. They do not need gases, and they are just as easy to use.

Residents of Los Angeles drive 142 million miles – the distance from Earth to
Mars – every day.

13. RUN YOUR CAR EFFICIENTLY

BACKGROUND. We all know that cars have a serious impact on the environment, but because we depend on them in our daily lives, it is unrealistic to suggest that people stop driving altogether (see p86 for suggestions on driving less).

Even if you drive every day, there is something simple you can do to help the earth: make sure your car is running as efficiently as possible. Getting good petrol mileage is not just a matter of economics – a fuel-efficient vehicle is actually less destructive to our planet than a petrol hog.

DID YOU KNOW
● Worldwide, there are an estimated 500 million motor vehicles in use today, about 350 million are cars. In Britain alone there are around 23 million petrol-driven vehicles.

● Annually UK road transport emits about 105 million tonnes – 18 percent of total emissions – of carbon dioxide (CO_2), the key ingredient in the greenhouse effect.

● The amount of CO_2 a car emits is directly related to the amount of petrol it uses.

● Road vehicles also cause acid rain by emitting nitrogen oxide. They were responsible for the release of 1.108 million tons in 1988, 45 percent of total emissions. This figure would be reduced by burning less petrol.

● Annually, Europe gives out 550,000 tonnes of hydrocarbons into the air, of which about a quarter come from road vehicles. These cause tree-killing and lung-damaging ozone smog. This is directly related to the amount of fuel consumed.

● Around 4.5 million tonnes of poisonous carbon monoxide are released in Britain every year, about 83 percent coming from motor vehicles. Again, this can be lessened by cutting down on petrol usage.

SIMPLE THINGS TO DO

● Keep your car tuned up. It is the easiest way to make your car more fuel efficient. A well-tuned car uses up to 9 percent less petrol than a poorly tuned car. That means 9 percent fewer toxic emissions.

● Keep track of your petrol mileage. If there is a sudden drop, you can detect it and get the problem fixed quickly.

SIMPLE PETROL SAVERS

● Do not let your car idle unnecessarily. It takes less petrol to start a car than it takes to let it idle. Idling becomes less efficient than restarting your car after about a minute.

● Keep fuel filters clean. Clogged filters use more petrol.

● Stay light. Check to see whether you are hauling around unnecessary weight in your car. Surprisingly, an extra 100lbs will decrease your fuel economy by more than 1 percent.

IF YOU ARE BUYING A NEW CAR

● Check the fuel economy figures and compare specifications.

● Keep fuel efficiency in mind. Remember, a car that gets 26.5 mpg will emit 20 tonnes less carbon dioxide in its lifetime than the average car on the road today. You can now buy cars that get almost 55 mpg, and some prototypes – the Toyota AXV, for example – can get up to 100 mpg.

● Weigh options carefully. Optional equipment like power steering and automatic transmissions need a lot of energy to run. Other extras like electric motor-driven windows or power brakes do not use as much, but still add to a car's weight and reduce fuel economy.

RESULTS

Little things help. For example, if 100,000 car owners who had neglected tuneups started getting their cars tuned up regularly, some 90 million pounds of carbon dioxide could be kept out of the atmosphere every year.

The average car consumes over 2,250 gallons of fuel in its lifetime.

14. RECHARGE YOUR BATTERIES

BACKGROUND. Household batteries that are thrown out with the garbage are taken to landfills, where they corrode and break apart, releasing dangerous mercury or cadmium into the soil. Batteries that are incinerated with garbage release mercury or cadmium into the air.

DID YOU KNOW

● Every year around 400 million batteries are sold in Britain.

● Prolonged exposure to mercury can not only make people extremely sick, but can even affect behaviour. In the 1600s hat-makers who used mercury to treat felt and fur began acting strangely. Since no one knew that the hatters were showing the effects of mercury poisoning, it was assumed that they were just crazy. Hence the expression 'mad as a hatter', and Alice's Mad Hatter.

● In France batteries account for over 80 percent of domestic mercury emissions.

● The production of mercury oxide batteries is prohibited in Denmark.

● Around 30 percent of the cadmium used worldwide goes into batteries.

SIMPLE THINGS TO DO

● Preferably, use mercury-free or cadmium-free batteries, which have recently come on the market.

● Use rechargeable batteries. Although they do contain cadmium, they last 500 times longer than alkaline batteries, thus they contribute a little less to our hazardous waste problem.

● Use mains power instead of batteries wherever possible.

● Never attempt to burn or puncture batteries.

How much garbage will you generate in your lifetime? About 600 times your adult weight.

15. IT'S NOT MY BAG?

BACKGROUND. We take it for granted that every time we go shopping, we will be given a bag in which to carry our purchases. But do we really need the millions of bags we use annually?

PAPER OR PLASTIC?

• Plastic shopping bags are often more convenient than paper, but they are not degradable. Even the 'biodegradable' plastic bags never completely disappear, they just break up into little pieces. And all plastic is made from petroleum, a non-renewable resource.

• Plastic bags often end up in the sea and kill marine animals that get tangled up in them or swallow them.

• The ink used on plastic bags contains cadmium, a toxic heavy metal. So when printed plastic bags are incinerated, heavy metals are spewed into the air.

• Paper bags are reusable and biodegradable.

SIMPLE THINGS TO DO

• Paper or plastic? Think twice before taking any bag if your purchase is small. If every shopper took just one less bag each month, we could save hundreds of millions of bags every year.

• Remember, all shopping bags are reusable.

• Even better, bring a cloth bag when you shop.

• When shopping for food, use string bags. They are easy to carry and fold up conveniently.

Every year, Britons use more than 2 billion toilet rolls.

16. FIND THE
HIDDEN TOXICS

BACKGROUND. Just because you bought something in a shop does not mean it is safe. There are a surprising amount of toxics in your home, hidden in everything from oven and drain cleaners to personal care products.

They are a hazard, not only to you and your family when they are used, but to the environment when they are first manufactured, and when they are finally disposed of.

What makes these products particularly insidious is the fact that millions of pounds are spent every year to convince us that they are necessary and will enhance our lives, when in fact they are dangerous.

Happily, there are many inexpensive, easy-to-use, natural alternatives that you can substitute for common commercial chemical products. It just takes a little detective work to find out which products you need to replace.

SIMPLE THINGS TO DO

● Remember, manufacturers do not have to declare toxics on their product labels. *C for Chemicals* by Michael Birkin and Brian Price (Green Print) contains good advice on toxic brands.

● Buy or make alternative products.
If you use alternatives, you reduce the risk of your family and the environment. Here are a few examples.

Toxic: no-iron fabrics. These are treated with formaldehyde resin, which becomes part of the fibre due to the way it is applied. Result: toxic fumes.
Alternative: natural fibres wherever possible.

Toxic: oven cleaners. These contain sodium hydroxide.
Alternative: sprinkle water, followed by layers of baking soda. Rub gently with very fine steel wool pads for tough spots.

Americans buy, and throw away, 500 million cigarette lighters every year.

Toxic: air fresheners. They do not actually freshen air, they deaden your nasal passages or coat them with oil. They may contain chemicals like xylene, ethanol, napthalene etc.
Alternative: herbal mixtures or vinegar and lemon juice.

Toxic: mothballs. These are made from paradichlorobenzene, which is harmful to your liver and kidneys.
Alternative: herbal products that act as repellents, cedar chips or cedar oil.

Toxic: permanent-ink pens and markers. Contain harmful solvents like toluene, xylene, ethanol.
Alternative: water-based markers and pens.

Tropical rainforests: every minute an area equal to 20 soccer pitches is lost.

17. LOOK OUT FOR YOUR LAWN

BACKGROUND. Lawn care is not something you normally associate with saving the earth, but, if you have a lawn, it is worthwhile to learn a few environmentally sound ways of taking care of it.

SIMPLE THINGS TO DO

● Keep lawnmower blades sharp. Blunt blades tear grass, instead of cutting it cleanly, which weakens it and will make your lawn more susceptible to weeds and disease.

● During dry periods, leave grass cuttings on the lawn. This works well if you keep grass long and cut small amounts each time. Cuttings will serve a moisture-retentive mulch and a natural fertiliser.

● At other times, use grass clippings and other lawn and garden waste to make a compost heap. It will provide your garden with natural mulch and fertiliser, and help reduce contributions to your local landfill.

● During the summer, water from sprinklers evaporates 4 to 8 times faster during the heat of the day than in the early morning. Watering at night is better than midday – there is no evaporation problem – but it can cause fungus in the grass. The best time to water is early morning.

● In a drought, do not waste water on grass beginning to turn brown. It is dormant and will revive after normal rainfall resumes.

● A green, healthy lawn is possible without pesticides and chemicals. Organic compost, for instance, is better for your soil than artificial fertiliser. Remember, too, that moss on lawns is usually caused by bad drainage, which moss killer will not cure.

Around 25 pints of tree-killing solvent can be emitted into the atmosphere when a single car is painted.

18. STAMP OUT STYROFOAM

BACKGROUND. What we think of as 'styrofoam' is actually polystyrene foam. This material is made from benzene (a known carcinogen), converted to styrene, and then injected with gases that make it a 'foam' product. The gases often used are CFCs, which eat ozone molecules, depleting the earth's vital ozone layer. The alternatives to CFCs at present are not wonderful. One is HCFC, 95 percent less damaging than CFCs, but still a threat to the ozone layer. Others are pentane and butane, hydrocarbons that contribute to urban smog. So non-CFC foam merely replaces one kind of environmental problem with another.

IT'S GARBAGE

● Polystyrene foam is completely non-biodegradable, it just will not go away. Even 500 years from now, that foam cup in which you had your coffee this morning might be sitting on the earth's surface.

● Because of its very structure – it contains large amounts of air – all styrofoam, regardless of how it is made, takes up a lot of space for its weight. This means that it wastes enormous amounts of precious space at already-bulging dumps.

● Polystyrene foam is deadly to marine life. It floats on sea surfaces, breaks up into pellets resembling food, and is consumed. When turtles, for example, eat styrofoam, its buoyancy keeps them from diving and clogs their systems so that they starve to death.

SIMPLE THINGS TO DO

● There is no such thing as safe polystyrene foam. Do not use it. Avoid foam packaging in egg cartons, delicatessen tubs etc.

● If you eat at fast food restaurants, ask for paper cups and plates.

Each year, pet cats kill around 100 million birds and mammals.

19. FIGHT THEM ON THE BEACHES

BACKGROUND. Our oceans provide most of the planet's oxygen, moisture and weather patterns. Without healthy oceans, life as we know it would end. Yet we have treated them as if they were expendable.

DID YOU KNOW

● Britain's beaches compare very unfavourably with those of Europe. Health risks prevail, and wildlife habitats are under threat.

● The European Blue Flag is awarded to those beaches that meet a standard of cleanliness and litter control, with good provisions for safety and environmental education. In 1987 only 17 of our beaches were worthy of the award.

● Each year, discarded ropes, nets and plastic waste kill over 2 million seabirds, 100,000 marine mammals, and large numbers of turtles and fish.

● 6 million tonnes of plastic – including discarded fishing gear – glass, tin, wood and food waste are dumped into the sea every year by ships.

SIMPLE THINGS TO DO

● Collecting plastic on the beach saves lives, so next time you go to a beach, take a rubbish bag. Then spend a few minutes picking up any litter you find.

● If you live near to a beach, or regularly visit the seaside, why not register with the Marine Conservation Society, 9 Gloucester Road, Ross-on-Wye, Herefordshire HR9 5BU. They run campaigns for people to help them monitor beaches. Each time you go to the beach, you fill in details of any pollution you find on a survey form. The MCS runs campaigns each year to 'highlight the often disgusting state of our beaches.'

Remember, detergents are available without chlorine.

20. BUYER BEWARE

BACKGROUND. Today a staggering 10 percent of all species of life on earth are endangered. In the quest for more profits, we are even threatening cherished creatures like elephants and dolphins. As a consumer, your power derives from what you decide to purchase. Use that power to protect wildlife.

DID YOU KNOW

● Ten years ago, there were 1.5 million elephants in Africa. Today, largely because they are being slaughtered for ivory, there are only 750,000. The elephant may become extinct by the year 2000.

● Over a million sea urchins a year are taken from the sea in Cornwall to be used as decorations or lamp shades.

● Big cats, leopards, tigers and lions are endangered through the purchase of skins, fur coats, hats and rugs.

● More than 6.5 million dolphins have been needlessly killed by tuna fishermen. Using circular purse seine nets up to three-quarters of a mile long, the fishermen surround an entire school of tuna, then draw the net closed at the bottom and pull it out of the water. Anything caught in the net dies. Dolphins, which travel with yellowfin tuna, are being hauled in and slaughtered en masse.

SIMPLE THINGS TO DO

● Do not buy ivory – not for any reason, under any circumstances. Do not buy tortoiseshell, coral, reptile skins, cat skins, or other products from endangered animals.

● Buy only bonita and skipjack tuna. At your local supermarket make a point of asking which tins of tuna do not involve the massacre of dolphins. Eventually, the message will get through. Remember, boycotts work – recently, Iceland gave up some whaling as a result of a boycott of its fish.

80% of tortoises imported to Britain perish while being shipped or within their first year here.

21. PESTS AND PETS

BACKGROUND. Of course, you do not want your dogs or cats to have fleas, but you do not want them to wear dangerous pesticides around their necks, either. Manufacturing and disposing of these products can threaten the environment, and create long-term health risks for all of us. Fortunately, there are effective alternatives.

DID YOU KNOW

● The sheer number of flea collars used and thrown away every year, make them a potent force.

● The pesticide on some flea collars finds its effectiveness in permanent nerve damage. The pet absorbs the chemical into its system until its tissue reeks of the toxin, and paralyses the bugs.

● Chemicals found in some pet collars include piperomylbutoxide (prolonged exposure to which can cause liver damage); DDVP – dichlorvos (which can cause cancer, nerve damage and mutations in animals); and carbaryl (which may cause birth defects in dogs).

SIMPLE THINGS TO DO
Some flea collar alternatives:

● Put orange or grapefruit skins through a food blender or processor, then simmer with some water. When the pulp is cool, brush into your pet's fur with your hands. Remember to use only skins, as fruit juice will make fur too sticky.

● Try adding brewer's yeast to your pet's food. In some cases, this is reportedly very effective.

● Ask for products containing methoprene, a growth inhibitor that interferes with flea larvae development.

● During the flea season, try a weekly flea bath.

Britons spend about £30 million a year on garden pesticides.

22. RECYCLE YOUR MOTOR OIL

BACKGROUND. Car manufacturers recommend that we change the oil in our cars every 6,000 miles. But they do not tell us what to do with the old oil. Used motor oil is perhaps the worst oil for the environment – while it is flowing through your engine it picks up all kinds of extra toxins.

DID YOU KNOW

● When used motor oil is poured into the ground, it can seep into the groundwater and contaminate drinking water supplies. Just 2 pints of motor oil can pollute over 200,000 gallons of drinking water.

● Pouring oil down the drain is like pouring it directly into a stream or a river. Just one pint of used motor oil can create a poisonous oil slick an acre in diameter.

● Throwing oil into the garbage is essentially the same as pouring it out. The oil will be dumped in a landfill, where it will eventually seep into the ground.

● About 17.5 million gallons of waste oil are produced by private motorists in the UK each year.

● Most recycled oil is reprocessed and sold as fuel for ships and industrial boilers. The rest is processed into lubricating and industrial oils.

SIMPLE THINGS TO DO

● If you get your oil changed at a garage, check first to make sure they plan to recycle it. If not, ask them to consider providing such a service and take your car somewhere where they do.

● If you change oil yourself, recycle it by taking it to your local civic amenity site. From there it will be transported to a refinery for reprocessing.

Every 3 months the US throws away enough aluminium to rebuild their entire
commercial airfleet.

23. GIVE GREEN

BACKGROUND. Most of us have difficulty at one time or another choosing presents for our families and friends. Often people are coaxed into a last-minute decision and pick something that is either inappropriate or damaging to the environment – or both.

Many gifts are over-packaged or ecologically harmful in their manufacture.

DID YOU KNOW

● Despite vigorous campaigning by animal rights groups, each year in the UK 21,000 animals are experimented on to test cosmetics and toiletries.

● 100,000 animals are killed annually in the US for the same reason.

SIMPLE THINGS TO DO

● If you are buying cosmetics, look for the 'Cruelty-Free' rabbit to avoid brands that have been tested on animals.

● One way of getting people interested in ecology is to give them specifically environmentally sound gifts, like subscriptions to green organisations. In addition, a number of bodies now provide a wide range of attractive products, the profits from which are channelled back into the environment. Some of them sell cards and wrapping paper that have been printed on recycled paper. You can even get gift tokens. Here are a few names – their products can be obtained by mail order:
Friends of the Earth, 26–28 Underwood Street, London N1 7JQ
Greenpeace UK, 30–31 Islington Green, London N1 8BR
Lifeline, 45 Shelton Street, London WC2 9HJ
Oxfam, Oxfam House, 274 Banbury Road, Oxford OX2 7DZ
Traidcraft PLC, Kingsway, Gateshead, Tyne and Wear NE11 0NE

Annually in the UK, 450 million animals are killed for food.

24. TUNE UP THE HEAT

BACKGROUND. The most important thing that people can do to save energy in their homes is to make sure their boilers are running efficiently. More domestic energy is used for heating than for any other purpose.

DID YOU KNOW

● Nearly 70 percent of the energy we use in the home is for heating rooms.

● The average home in Britain costs between £300 and £400 to keep warm.

● In 1988 155,000 tons of sulphur dioxide, 4 percent of the national emission total, was released from British households.

● About 27 percent of British carbon dioxide emissions come from domestic space heating.

SIMPLE THINGS TO DO

● Your heating bill can be reduced by about 8 percent for every 1°C you turn your temperature thermostat down.

● The Energy Efficiency Office recommends that boilers are tuned up once a year. This could cut down your energy use by 5 percent. British Gas runs schemes for the aftercare of boilers.

● Make some reflectors by taping aluminium foil to pieces of cardboard, then place them behind your radiators. This saves energy and money by throwing back heat you would normally have lost through the walls.

It takes half a gallon of water to cook a pot of pasta, and a gallon to wash the pot.

25. LIGHT RIGHT

BACKGROUND. The simple action of turning a light switch on and off affects the environment. The more electricity we use, the more industrial emissions we generate, contributing heavily to problems like the greenhouse effect and acid rain.

There are several simple ways to 'light right'. The most obvious is conservation – diligently turning lights off when they are not in use. But a less obvious, and more effective, method is to choose and use your lightbulbs with energy conservation in mind.

LIGHT READING

● An ordinary 100W light bulb has about a thousand hour life. During that time it will consume about £7 worth of electricity.

● Most people are unaware of the development of the compact fluorescent light bulb. This amazing bulb screws into the standard sockets, and gives off light that looks just like a traditional bulb – not like the fluorescents we are used to seeing in factories, schools and offices.

● Compact fluorescents are big energy-savers. They last ten times longer and use about 75 percent less electricity than an ordinary bulb.

● Substituting a compact fluorescent bulb for a traditional bulb will keep half a tonne of carbon dioxide out of the atmosphere over the life of the bulb.

● Compact fluorescents are more expensive to buy than traditional bulbs. But studies have shown that the real cost of an ordinary bulb is the initial price, plus 5 to 10 times the cost in electricity. So the cost of a compact fluorescent will generally wind up saving money as well as the environment.

● Compact fluorescents are not suitable for every type of lighting situation. One factor is size – they will not work in small lamps and certain covered fixtures. Another factor is frequency of use. They make the most sense if they are used in places where they are left on for at least 2 hours a day. Also, at low temperatures, the life of a compact fluorescent can be reduced, so enclose the bulb in a glass fitting if you are using it outside.

RESULTS
If a single compact fluorescent bulb was installed in each of 1 million houses, the energy equivalent of about 600,000 traditional bulbs would be saved.

BRIGHT IDEAS
• Interestingly, one large ordinary bulb is more efficient than two small ones in a multi-bulb fixture. A 100W bulb, for example, generates about as much light as two 60W bulbs, and it saves energy.

• In light fixtures that take three bulbs, try using only two. But for safety's sake, put a burned-out bulb in the last socket.

• Try more efficient bulbs such as long-life, krypton-filled, tungsten halogen and infrared-reflective coated.

Energy-saving tip: keep light bulbs and shades clean – dirt absorbs light and uses more energy.

26. DON'T LET GO

BACKGROUND. In 1985 an emaciated 17-foot female sperm whale died on the New Jersey coast. When marine scientists examined it, they found a balloon, with 3 feet of ribbon still attached to it, blocking the valve that connected the whale's stomach to its intestines. Because the whale had swallowed the balloon, it was unable to digest food, and it was starving to death. Since then, similar incidents have been recorded, notably with turtles that died after swallowing partly-deflated rubber balloons.

DID YOU KNOW

• When balloons land in the water, they quickly lose their colour. With ribbons or strings trailing behind them, they look uncannily like jellyfish, which are a favourite food of turtles.

• Depending on the wind, balloons can travel for hundreds of miles before they finally land.

• Schools of squid, the sperm whale's favourite food, congregate around pieces of plastic in the water. When they surround a rubber balloon, whales will swallow that too.

• As mylar (metallic) balloons float into the air, they can get caught up in power lines and cause power failure.

LOFTY IDEAS

• If you buy helium-filled balloons, hold on to them, and do not release them into the atmosphere when you have finished with them.

• If you attend an event where balloons are released, write to the organisers and inform them of the potential hazards.

Only 3% of the earth's water is fresh water.

TAKING
A LITTLE

EFFORT

27. REUSE OLD NEWS

BACKGROUND. 2 million tonnes of waste paper are recycled annually in the UK. If we doubled this, we would spare 30 million trees.

DID YOU KNOW

• It takes 15 trees to make 1 tonne of virgin paper.

• To produce Britain's paper and board, the pulp from more than 130 million trees is used. That is more than two trees per head.

• 8.7 million tonnes of paper are consumed in Britain annually.

• Making new paper from old paper uses only 10 percent of the water and 50 percent of the energy used in making paper from trees, and it reduces related air pollution by over 75 percent.

• Recycled paper could easily be substituted for virgin paper in many products without any loss in quality, but because the demand for it has been low, recycled paper prices tend to be higher than virgin stock. This, in turn, makes it harder to get. Result: manufacturers that could use recycled paper do not bother.

• The markets for high-grade waste paper are reliable and tend not to fluctuate. Wastepaper merchants grade paper according to type, from computer-listing paper (top grade) to newspaper, magazines and cardboard. Again, because current demand is limited, some waste paper collected may still have to be dumped. If we bought more paper recycled from the lower grades, then wastepaper merchants could sell off their glut.

• Recycled paper is usually cheaper than its virgin equivalents in both Holland and Germany.

• The UK recycles only 35 percent of its paper, in Holland the figure is 50 percent.

Drinking water generally contains more than 16 toxic pesticides.

SIMPLE THINGS TO DO

● Newspapers are probably the easiest material to recycle, since they lie around the house anyway. Recycling them is a simple way to get into the recycling habit. But remember that other types of paper and card are recyclable, too.

1. Save them

● Do not throw newspapers out with the garbage anymore.

● Sort them. Magazines, with their coloured paper and coated covers, are not easily recyclable.

● Stack them. The key to a personal recycling programme is to have a place in your home where the newspapers always go.

2. Recycle them

● Look in the Yellow Pages to find your local paper merchant. Ask which types of paper are most in demand, and whether a container loan for one morning a month is possible.

● Otherwise, drop paper off in the designated receptacles at supermarkets, shopping centres, recycling centres etc. The Daily Telegraph/Friends of the Earth *Recycling Directory* will tell you the whereabouts of your nearest paper collection point.

3. Create a demand for recycled paper by requesting it at your stationers.

Recyclers: robins like to use small lengths of string in their nests.

28. RECYCLE GLASS

BACKGROUND. People have been making glass for approximately 3,500 years. Most glass is made of three basic ingredients: white sand, soda and lime.

The materials are heated to around 1,200°C, until they are completely dissolved and transparent. Then the mixture is cooled to around 900°C. The whole process takes about 7,600 BTUs of energy to produce a single pound of glass.

Before recycled glass is shipped to the manufacturers, it is broken so it will take up less volume. This broken glass is called cullet.

When it arrives at the factory, cullet is run through a magnetic device designed to remove rings from bottles. A vacuum process removes plastic coatings and paper labels, then the cullet is ready to be added to the mixture.

Because cullet lowers the melting temperature of the mixture in manufacturing glass, up to 32 percent less energy is required. This is a huge amount when you consider how much glass we produce every year.

DID YOU KNOW

• Annually, we use about 6 billion bottles and jars, which is the equivalent of over 1.5 million tonnes of glass.

• The energy saved from recycling one glass bottle will light a 100W bulb for four hours.

• All glass bottles and jars can be recycled. But other types of glass, such as window panes, pyrex and light bulbs, are made by different processes and cannot be combined with the cullet from which glass containers are made.

• Every tonne of recycled glass saves 30 gallons of oil required for processing from raw materials. In 1987, the UK actually imported 12,000 tonnes of European glass.

• The British Glass Manufacturers Confederation hope to increase the number of bottle banks to one for every 10,000 people by 1991.

Reuse is even better than recycling: the average milk bottle is used 33 times.

• We now have around 4,000 local authority bottle banks, through which some 16 percent of our glass containers are recycled.

• 31 percent of glass is recycled in Europe; Holland recycles 62 percent. Britain is second from bottom in the league table of European glass recycling.

• Glass produced from recycled glass instead of raw material reduces related air pollution by 20 percent and water pollution by 50 percent.

• Because glass takes so long to decompose, the bottle you throw away today may still be littering the landscape in the year 3000.

SIMPLE THINGS TO DO

• The easiest way to recycle glass at home is to organise your garbage so that you can separate and save bottles in a convenient way, either indoors or outdoors.

• For example, keep a box for glass in a cupboard, or buy a plastic rubbish bin to keep outside. Store the glass as you use it.

• Sort bottles according to colour: clear, green and brown.

• Remove any corks or metal caps which cannot be removed magnetically. Do not worry about paper labels.

• Rinsing is sometimes suggested, but is not absolutely necessary – ask at your local recycling centre.

• Once you have a place to put the bottles as you use them, it only takes about 15 minutes a week to keep up the recycling.

• Not enough glass is being recycled in this country. Encourage your local authority to increase the amount of bottle banks in your area. You should also lobby your supermarket to promote the return of bottles for recycling. One way would be to stock more bottles that require deposits.

The trade in animal furs is still continuing at around 20 million furs per year.

29. DON'T CAN IT

BACKGROUND. Aluminium is the world's most abundant metal, but it was only discovered in the 1820s. At that time it was worth more than gold. The first aluminium drink can appeared in 1963, and this now accounts for the largest single use of aluminium.

DID YOU KNOW

- Because Britain does not have economically viable deposits of aluminium ore, we have to import aluminium. It is therefore vital that we recycle.

- When you throw out one aluminium can you waste as much energy as you would have if you had filled the same can half-full of petrol and poured it down the drain.

- Britain uses over 13 billion cans a year, around half of which are aluminium and half tin-plated steel. Less than 2 percent are recycled.

- Every year we throw away about 2.5 million tonnes of metal, which would be worth more than £1 billion.

- The production of aluminium is highly energy-intensive – to make 1 tonne requires 4 tonnes of bauxite.

- Recycling aluminium cuts related air pollution by 95 percent.

- Making aluminium recycled from aluminium uses 95 percent less energy than making aluminium from scratch.

- If you throw an aluminium can out of your car window, it will still litter the earth up to 500 years later.

- If you throw away 2 aluminium cans, you waste more energy than is used daily by each of a billion human beings in the developing world.

- In 1988 alone, aluminium can recycling in the US saved more than 11 billion kilowatt hours of electricity, enough to supply the residential needs of the city of New York for 6 months.

If everyone in Britain placed one day's rubbish in Trafalgar Square, the pile would reach up to Nelson's feet.

• The energy saved from one recycled aluminium can will operate a television set for 3 hours.

SIMPLE THINGS TO DO

• The simplest way of extracting steel cans from your rubbish is by using a magnet. At present, there are only 24 local authorities that use magnets to reclaim steel cans. If more councils extracted steel in this way, then virtually every steel can could be recycled. We must lobby councils to introduce steel recycling schemes.

• Aluminium recycling is a profitable business, worth over £500 per tonne. However, the recycling of aluminium is yet to really take off here – there are so far only around 200 local authority aluminium can banks.

• Find out where the can banks are in your area by ringing the local council.

• If there are facilities for recycling steel cans in your area, then separate them out.

• Remove food, rinse the cans, and then crush them to save space.

• Remember that these aluminium items can also be recycled: kitchen foil, ring pulls, cigarette foil (extract the paper), foil baking containers, and the foil from milk bottle tops and yoghurt tops.

Contrary to popular belief, small appliances such as blenders and carving knives do not add much to your electricity bill.

30. PRECYCLE

BACKGROUND. In 1989, the city government of Berkeley, California, initiated a campaign to encourage consumers to buy food packaged in biodegradable or recyclable materials. They called it 'precycling'.

DID YOU KNOW

● Every week the average British family buys more than 56lbs of packaged groceries. Around a third of it is packaging, which we discard as soon as the package is opened.

● Around 6 percent of household refuse is made up of plastic, 900,000 tonnes a year.

● About 25 percent of all plastics and around 50 percent of the paper produced in this country are used for packaging.

● Britons consume over 2.5 million tonnes of plastic every year.

SIMPLE THINGS TO DO

● Keep your eyes open when you shop. Everything you buy has an effect on the environment – try to make it a positive one. Here are some simple examples of precycling:

● Buy eggs in recycled cardboard, rather than styrofoam, cartons.

● Most cereal boxes are made of recycled cardboard. It is easy to tell – the boxes are grey on the inside.

● Buy in bulk. It is cheaper, and uses less packaging.

● Buy drinks in glass containers, which are easy to recycle. You can also choose sauces, baby foods, spreads etc. that are packaged in glass instead of plastic.

● Avoid plastic containers, especially 'squeezable' ones, which are made up of different types of plastic in several layers, and are dramatically non-biodegradable.

Just one part oil per million parts water will make drinking water smell and taste funny.

31. USE CLOTH NAPPIES

BACKGROUND. In 1961, Procter and Gamble introduced the first affordable disposable nappy, Pampers. To most parents, it seemed like a triumph of modern technology – a clean, convenient way to deal with an unpleasant, messy problem.

It was an instant financial bonanza for Procter and Gamble, too. Other brands soon appeared, and today there are dozens of varieties to choose from. But along with them comes indisputable evidence that disposable nappies are taking a serious toll on the environment.

DID YOU KNOW

● Britain's babies get through 3.5 billion disposable nappies every year.

● Disposable nappies use the wood from 30 million trees each year.

● Manufacturers recommend that people wash out disposable nappies before discarding them, but very few do. This means that every year, millions of tonnes of soiled, potentially disease-infected nappies are dumped into landfills.

● The contamination of groundwater by viruses is, therefore, a big potential problem. More than 100 different intestinal viruses are known to be excreted in human faeces, including polio and hepatitis. Fortunately, no groundwater contamination of this nature has been discovered yet. But as the build-up increases, it may be just a matter of time.

● Degradable disposable nappies do not seem to be the answer. They do decompose faster than standard disposables because they have a cornstarch base, so that the plastic breaks into little pieces. But they take up the same space in landfills, and the health risks are the same.

Reuse is even better than recycling: use plastic cartons for seedlings.

NOT SO SIMPLE THINGS TO DO

This is a tough one, not because there is any question of what we ought to do, but because it is hard to give up disposable nappies.

If you are ready for terry nappies:
Cloth nappies are available at Mothercare.

If you have difficulty switching to terry nappies:
● Remember, it does not have to be all or nothing. It is better to alternate between terry nappies and disposables than to use disposables exclusively.

● If you must use disposable nappies, opt for chlorine-free (non-bleached) brands.

If you are using terry nappies, you will need nappy covers:
● Cloth nappies do not absorb moisture the way disposable nappies do, so you will need nappy covers to act as a shield between the nappy and the rest of the world. Natural fibres are best, and if you want to make them yourself, 100 percent wool felt seems to be the ideal fabric. It offers 'complete breathability', and does not irritate the baby.

HM Inspectorate of Pollution has found that over 1,000 English and Welsh landfills are threatened by explosion.

32. PUT IT TO WORK AT WORK

BACKGROUND. Most of the things that you have been working on at home apply in the work place, too. It is not always easy to implement them, but it is worth it. An enormous amount of the earth's resources are consumed at businesses, and an enormous amount can be saved. You may even get that long-awaited pay rise, because recycling can save your company a fortune.

DID YOU KNOW
• Each tonne of recycled paper saves more than 3 cubic yards of landfill space.
• Every tonne of recycled office paper saves about 350 gallons of oil.
• Every year, Americans throw away enough office and writing paper to build a wall 12 feet high, stretching from New York to Los Angeles.

SIMPLE THINGS TO DO
By yourself. It is easy to do some little things on your own. Here are some examples:
• Bring a coffee cup to work instead of using disposable cups.
• Reuse manila envelopes by putting sticky labels over the old addresses. Any stationer should have them.

Projects to work on with your colleagues:
• Set up glass and aluminium can recycling programmes. This usually entails putting containers for saving bottles and cans in a prominent place, and organising a rota to decide who takes them to the recycling centre when they are full.
• Set up a special environmental bulletin board and post notices with interesting titbits and statistics about conservation. Include photographs where appropriate.

To produce one pat of butter, almost 100 gallons of water are required.

- Substitute paper cups, which are biodegradable, for styrofoam cups, which are not.

- Set up a paper recycling programme. There is a simple procedure. Each employee saves paper at their desk. The trick is to sort paper into recyclable groups as it is discarded, by using desktop containers. Then a collection system is introduced. Friends of the Earth have started to sponsor such schemes in many offices.

- See if you can get a two-sided xerox machine. Or, if you have one already, make sure that everyone makes double-sided copies wherever possible. Thousands of pages can be saved when copying lengthy reports.

- Have an energy audit to assess your office's use of electricity, etc. It can make a huge difference.

- If some of your firm's company cars still unnecessarily run on leaded petrol, lobby your superiors.

Plywood and chipboard emit formaldehyde, one of the home's biggest indoor pollutants.

33. GET A CATALYTIC CONVERTER

BACKGROUND. Motor vehicles release enormous amounts of pollution into the atmosphere every day, and each ingredient in the cocktail of exhaust fumes has a separate effect on our environment.

Annually, British cars spew out 4.5 million tonnes of poisonous carbon monoxide, 100,000 tonnes of hydrocarbons (which can cause cancer), 2,500 tonnes of tetraethyl lead (which can cause brain damage), as well as huge quantities of nitrogen oxides (which react with hydrocarbons to make tree-killing smog) and carbon dioxide (which contributes to the greenhouse effect).

The catalytic converter can be built into the exhaust system, and has been developed to clean up the gases that cars emit.

DID YOU KNOW

● Catalytic converters cannot run on leaded petrol.

● In the US, where catalytic converters have become obligatory, the emission of nitrogen oxides and hydrocarbons from new cars has been reduced by 75 percent, and carbon monoxide by 90 percent.

● The world's biggest manufacturer of catalytic converters is actually a British firm, Johnson Matthey, who have to sell the vast majority of them abroad.

● Catalytic converters will not become compulsory in the UK for another two years. In the meantime, it is estimated that exhaust fumes will have risen by a further 5 percent.

SIMPLE THINGS TO DO

● See if your present car can be fitted with a catalytic converter. And, when you buy your next car, find out which models have them. Johnson Matthey will be able to help. Their address is: Johnson Matthey Catalytic Systems Division, Orchard Road, Royston, Hertfordshire SG8 5HE.

The EC's Environmental Task Force has estimated that after 1992 European road freight will increase by 30%.

34. RECYCLE THE REST

BACKGROUND. Although paper, glass and, to some extent, aluminium, are commonly recycled, they are not the only materials that can be recycled.

SIMPLE THINGS TO DO

• Visit your local civic amenity site and find out what can be recycled there. They generally have facilities for paper, card, cans, glass, oil, metal and rags.

• Remember, another form of recycling is to take good care of your possessions. If they break or wear out, do not automatically throw them away. Consider getting them mended. When they do eventually outlast their usefulness you can give them away, to a charity or jumble sale. Only when they cannot be reused should they be recycled.

PLASTIC

So far in Britain plastic recycling has not been widespread. This is because there are so many different types, both of varying composition and quality, and the industry has found it difficult to separate them economically. A mixture of varying types of plastic will only recycle into low grade products.

There are, however, around 60 companies that have embarked on a plastic recycling programme, reclaiming between them over 150,000 tonnes per year. The Information Bureau at the British Plastics Federation, 5 Belgrave Square, London SW1X 8PH, will be willing to give you a list of the companies involved in your area.

A useful booklet that gives general information on voluntary collections of most materials is obtainable from the National Anti-Waste Programme, Ashdown House, 123 Victoria Street, London SW1E 6RB.

By the year 2000 America hopes to be recycling 42% of its plastic refuse.

35. TURN YOUR GARDEN INTO A WILDLIFE REFUGE

BACKGROUND. Helping to save and care for animals can begin in your own garden. By landscaping and planting with wildlife in mind, you can make up for the loss of much of their natural habitat. Simply by choosing the right plants, you can provide them with their natural food and shelter. And you will have the benefit of a window onto the natural world.

DID YOU KNOW

● A recent study of the gardens at Buckingham Palace discovered that 10 percent of all the known animal species in Britain can be found there.

● Your garden may contain as many as 300 different species of animal life.

SIMPLE THINGS TO DO

● You can attract specific animals to your garden with certain plants. Birds, for example, like honeysuckle, rowan and crab apples; butterflies are attracted to brightly coloured flowers, like gentians or buttercups.

● Animals like to shelter in hedges and shrubs, rather than behind fences and walls.

● Birds are often desperate for water in the winter, when the ground is frozen. A regular supply of warm water in a birdbath can help hundreds of birds to survive.

● You can set up a bird feeder on a town balcony as well as a country garden. Even if you have cats, there are safe ways to put up feeders.

Your old car battery is worth money when you trade it in for a new one.

36. HELP PROTECT THE RAINFORESTS

BACKGROUND. Some people consider the destruction of the world's rainforests the most frightening of all the recent ecological developments, perhaps because it is something that can be measured. The tropical rainforests, located in a narrow region near the equator in Africa, South and Central America, and Asia, are disappearing so fast that by the year 2000, 80 percent of them may be gone.

A tropical rainforest is technically defined as a forest in the tropics which receives 4 to 8 metres of rain per year. Beyond that, it is nature's laboratory for all kinds of plant, animal and insect life. The world's tropical rainforests are critical links in the ecological chain of life that makes up the planet's biosphere.

DID YOU KNOW

● Each year, 27 million acres of tropical rainforests are destroyed.

● Although rainforests make up only 2 percent of the earth's surface, over half the world's wild plant, animal and insect species live there. In a typical four-mile-square patch of tropical rainforest you would find: over 750 species of trees, over 1,500 different kinds of flowering plants, 125 different mammals, 400 kinds of birds, 100 reptiles, 60 amphibians and countless insects, including 150 types of butterfly. Only 1 percent of these species has ever been studied.

● It has been estimated that, as a result of the destruction, 50 species of wildlife are becoming extinct each day.

● 80 percent of all Amazonian deforestation has taken place since 1980.

● One in four pharmaceuticals comes from a plant in a tropical rainforest.

Americans produce enough styrofoam cups every year to circle the earth 436 times.

- About 70 percent of plants identified by the National Cancer Institute as being useful in the treatment of cancer are found only in rainforests, and 1,400 rainforest plants are believed to offer potential cures for cancer.
- Tropical rainforests produce oxygen and consume carbon dioxide. The rainforests of Amazonia produce about 40 percent of the world's oxygen.
- Latin America and Southeast Asia have already lost 40 percent of their tropical rainforests.
- Deforestation contributes between 10 and 30 percent of worldwide carbon dioxide emissions. In 1987, rainforest fires, one method of clearing, pumped about 530 million tonnes of carbon into the air, roughly one tenth of the total world fossil fuel combustion for that year.

WHAT HAPPENS TO RAINFORESTS

- The world's rainforests are being depleted as a result of several developments: agriculture and population resettlement; beef cattle ranching; major power projects like dams, hydro-electric plants, and the roads that go with them; and logging.
- The soil in rainforests is not rich. Only about a two-inch layer contains any nutrients. Most of a rainforest's nutrients are stored in the vegetation. When a rainforest is converted to, for example, cattle grazing, the soil is grazed out within two years. The cattle operation then moves on, and leaves a desert behind it.

WHAT YOU CAN DO

- This is more than a political cause, it is a fight to save a precious piece of the world. Who knows what may be discovered in the rainforests: an unknown plant that provides a cure for cancer? A new crop that can feed starving children? Unfortunately, the only real influence you may have is on the people who provide financial support to countries with rainforests. So write letters expressing your concern. The Gaia Foundation, 18 Well Walk, Hampstead, London NW3 1LD, will be able to furnish you with some addresses. Write to your MP.

It is estimated that the world's 1.3 billion cows annually produce nearly 90 million tonnes of methane.

● Support organisations involved in rainforest conservation. For example, the World Wide Fund for Nature is helping a project to safe-guard the oldest rainforest in Africa by protecting 1,300 kilometres of pristine forest in Cameroon. Find out more by writing to The Rainforest Programme, World Wide Fund for Nature, Panda House, Weyside Park, Godalming, Surrey GU7 1XR.

● Consider substitutes for tropical woods. More than 40 percent of the plywood in Britain is imported from tropical countries. Friends of the Earth's *The Good Wood Guide* has good advice on acceptable alternatives.

Around 32% of our drinking-quality water is flushed down the toilet.

37. THE GREAT ESCAPE

BACKGROUND. Since the energy crisis of the 1970s, experts have been telling us regularly that insulating is one of the best ways to save energy. You cannot take energy conservation seriously without making sure your home is properly insulated. It is not always simple, for it can take both time and money. But the savings on energy and fuel bills will make it worthwhile.

INSULATION FACTS

● It has been calculated by Friends of the Earth that, mostly through insulation, it would technically be possible to reduce our energy needs by as much as two-thirds.

● Heat escapes at more than three times the rate through solid wall construction than through modern walls. About 40 percent of British housing is of solid wall construction.

● Better home insulation could prevent the emission of up to 100 tonnes of the greenhouse gas, carbon dioxide, in the lifetime of a house.

Lofts

● Almost 80 percent of lofts have less than 1 centimetre of insulation. This does not make economic sense, and it is also below the standard required by the government for new homes.

● If you installed loft insulation you could save up to £100 per year on your heating bill. The same applies to cavity wall insulation.

Doors and Windows

● Draughts, around half of which come through undraught-proofed doors and windows, can account for as much as 25 percent of heat loss in your home. You could save as much as a tenth of your heating bill by draught-proofing.

● A quarter of your heat can be lost through single-glazed windows. Installing double-glazed windows could mean a 50 percent reduction of heat loss through your windows.

70 to 80 percent of the world's coastlines have eroded since 1900.

SIMPLE THINGS TO DO
Insulate:

● If there is no insulation in your home, you are costing yourself and the environment a fortune. If you do have insulation, check to see if you have enough. Rubber and plastic sealants, for draughtstripping and caulking around the home, can cost between £30 and £60. This will often be paid back in the first year in heating savings.

Have an energy audit to find the heat leaks in your house or flat:

● This can be done simply by going around the window and door frames of your home with a lighted candle. Be careful not to get near flammable material. If the flame flickers, there are substantial gaps allowing hot air out and cold air in. You need to caulk and draughtstrip.

● Or, have it done professionally. There are a number of local energy consultants who offer this service. Otherwise, try your local electricity board.

If you are doing your own energy audit:

● Pick a cold, windy day, when secret draughts and leaks will reveal themselves readily to the flame of a candle. An inspection should include more than just the outer walls, since the interior of your home will probably have leaks as well.

● Be sure to check everywhere for energy leaks. Cracks or holes in walls and ceilings, places where plumbing or wiring penetrates walls, floors and ceilings, attic doors etc.

● Windows also deserve special attention.

Common sense insulation: wear warm clothes, hang thick curtains.

38. PLANT A TREE

BACKGROUND. Trees have a very special part to play in the global warming equation because their growth is the only process that actually reduces atmospheric carbon dioxide.

Planting a tree is an effective way to fight the greenhouse effect, and it is easier than you may think.

DID YOU KNOW

● The average Briton uses the equivalent of at least 2 trees a year.

● 10,000 years ago, before agriculture, more than 15 billion acres worldwide were covered by forest. Today barely 10 billion acres are forested. Between 1950 and 1980, the forested surface of the earth was reduced by roughly 25 percent.

● In some places deforestation is proceeding at a runaway rate. In California, urban trees are dying or being removed at four times the replacement rate. Each year, 28 million acres of tropical forest are destroyed. Some countries, like Nigeria, which were once large lumber exporters, have become net importers.

● The interdependence between trees and human and animal life could not be more fundamental. We require oxygen and produce carbon dioxide, trees and other plants require carbon dioxide and produce oxygen. Any significant loss in forested land directly affects the earth's atmosphere for other forms of life.

● By consuming carbon dioxide, trees mitigate the greenhouse effect. It is estimated that each mature tree consumes, on average, about 13lbs of carbon dioxide per year. Urban trees consume it at a rate of about 15 times that of rural trees.

● The loss of a tree not only reduces carbon dioxide consumption, it also releases carbon dioxide stored in the tree. When a tree dies naturally, this CO_2 is released slowly; when it is cut or burned, the release is sudden and rapid, and harder for

One gallon of petrol can contaminate 750,000 gallons of water.

the atmosphere to absorb. Net worldwide tree loss accounts for about 25 percent of global carbon dioxide emissions.

● By providing shade and evaporative cooling, trees also affect local temperature. Again, urban trees even more than rural ones. Clusters of urban trees can cool ambient air temperature by 5°C. Moreover, the energy saved reduces global warming by about 15 times the amount of CO_2 absorbed by those trees.

SIMPLE THINGS TO DO

● If you would like to plant a tree, but do not know how to begin, visit a local nursery or horticultural society.
Tree-planting is a lot easier than you may think, and many people will not only be helpful, but enthusiastic.

● You may want to be part of the effort to replace the millions of elms lost to Dutch Elm Disease by ordering an immune elm from Pitney Bowes, The Pinnacles, Harlow, Essex CM19 5BD.

● Consider talking to your neighbours and friends to see if you can spread the word and launch a community-wide planting effort.

● Planting trees has a cumulative effect. Each tree you plant will provide benefits for years to come. For example, if only 100,000 people each plant a tree this year, the trees will still be absorbing over a million pounds of carbon dioxide annually in the year 2010. But if the same people plant a tree every year from now until 2010, the trees will absorb over 20 million pounds of CO_2 in that year.

How can you find a leak in your toilet? Put some dye in the tank and if the colour turns up in the bowl without a flush, you have a leak.

39. PREVENT PESTS NATURALLY

BACKGROUND. When DDT was introduced in the 1940s, it was regarded as a miracle. After thousands of years of fighting agricultural pests, human begins had finally devised a 'safe' way to keep them at bay. With DDT, scientists believed, agricultural land would become more productive and the world's hungry could be fed. But DDT proved to be toxic not only to insects, but to all life. Although banned in Britain, its illicit use is still believed to be widespread.

The DDT story is an apt metaphor for all chemical pesticides. Once it seemed ideal, now the evidence is mounting that it is an ecological disaster. It was designed to eliminate specific pests, but it often poisons birds and other wildlife instead. It seeps into groundwater and contaminates drinking water. It even destroys the soil itself by killing essential organisms, from microbes to earthworms. It is also harmful to humans, especially children.

Yet pesticide use grows.

Fortunately, there are effective natural alternatives to chemical pesticides. As consumers we should encourage farmers to use them, and we should learn to use them around our homes.

DID YOU KNOW

● Ironically, pesticides do not seem to be improving agricultural yield. Research has shown that farmers are still losing about the same percentage of their crops to pests as they did before the use of pesticides.

● Over 100 active pesticide ingredients are known to cause birth defects, cancer and gene mutation.

● Sooner or later, targeted pests develop resistance to specific pesticides, rendering the chemicals worthless. More than 440 species of insects and mites, and 70 types of fungus are now resistant to pesticides.

About 6 percent of your domestic rubbish is made up of plastic.

- Many home pesticides are just as lethal as agricultural ones.
- The 18 million gardeners in Britain cultivate a total of 1 million acres of land, and spend £20 million on garden chemicals every year.

SIMPLE THINGS TO DO
Learn about alternatives

- If you have to use a pesticide, use an organic one that will break down in the soil.
- Do not use 'all-purpose' pesticides.
- C for Chemicals by Mike Birkin and Brian Price has good advice on what products to avoid.

Buy organically grown produce

- Most supermarket chains now carry organically grown food – try it and taste the difference.
- If you cannot find organic produce, make a special request. You are not the only one who will be asking.

If you have mice in your house, a mousetrap is still the best way to catch them.

40. WHAT A WASTE

BACKGROUND. Most people do not know how to dispose of household hazardous wastes properly. Some of us, for example, innocently pour toxics down the drain into the sewer system, which might be the worst possible way to get rid of them, since waste water treatment plants are not specifically designed to handle hazardous material. The result could be serious water contamination.

Disposing of them in landfills does not work, either. Hazardous wastes dumped into a landfill can seep into the groundwater, run off into surface water, or pollute the air.

Since there are so many hazardous products in use, and because they can have such a lethal impact on the environment, it is important for us to learn what products we have, how to store them, and what to do when we have finished with them.

DID YOU KNOW

- It is illegal in the UK to tip sump oil down the sink.
- Hazardous wastes often found around the house include: paints and paint thinners, car batteries, oven and drain cleaners, mothballs, floor and furniture polish, brake or transmission fluid, antifreeze, carpet and upholstery cleaners, pesticides, and furniture strippers. Even some products to clean toilets are considered hazardous.

SIMPLE THINGS TO DO
Store hazardous materials properly:

- Keep them in their original containers. Do not risk the possibility of anyone else mistaking them or misusing them.
- Make sure labels are securely fixed to containers, so you know what they contain.
- Keep them in a cool, dry place, out of the reach of children.
- If the original container leaks, put the whole thing into a larger container, and do not forget to mark it.

Reusing is even better than recycling: use jars to store rice, sugar, pasta etc.

Try to reduce the amount of hazardous products you use:

● Buy exactly what you need. Remember, the more you buy, the more you have to dispose of. If you have some left over – paint, for example – share it with neighbours, friends and family. Try to use it up.

● Use safer substitutes wherever possible. For example, a strong solution of vinegar works well as a toilet cleaner, and a mixture of one part lemon juice to two parts olive oil is a good substitute wood polish.

Dispose of it properly:

● Recycle whenever possible. Used motor oil, car batteries and some solvents can be refined and reused. Your local authority should be able to help you identify recycling programmes.

● Municipal incineration is a way of dealing with some hazardous wastes. Never use incinerators at home – they do not work.

● Find a licenced contractor or recycling site. If your area does not have one then call your local wastewater treatment plant. They can advise you on the disposal of wastes.

Britons produce about 23 million tonnes of household refuse every year.

41. TRY CARSHARING

B ACKGROUND. The growing number of cars on the road poses an enormous threat to the environment. Yet for many, there are few alternatives to driving.

DID YOU KNOW
● It has been estimated that by the year 2000, Britain will have constructed another 900 miles of major roads and motorways, damaging Sites of Special Scientific Interest (SSSIs) and robbing the UK of even more countryside.
● 25 acres of land are consumed by each mile of a six-lane motorway.
● 54 percent of journeys made to work in the UK are made by car.
● 65 percent of people who need to travel for their work, do so by car.

SIMPLE THINGS TO DO
● Although carsharing has never been seriously considered in this country, some environmentalists believe that it may yet prove an effective way of cutting down on cars and their harmful by-products.
● Try setting up a carsharing programme in your area. If you make regular journeys – to work, for instance, or perhaps you visit a relative on the same day every week – place a notice in your local post office or newspaper. It is likely that at least one other person is making the same trip in another car.
● **Try a shared car ownership scheme:**
A number of families buy a car jointly and use it mainly for large loads or difficult journeys. All participants buy public transport passes, too, and each has a key to the car. Mileage is logged, and paid to the treasurer. One consequence may be that as people discover how much cheaper public transport is, so the car is used less and less. The pioneer of this scheme, Max Glaskin, can supply you with further information. Write to him at 9 St Paul's Street, Brighton BN2 3HR.

Scrap cars can be recycled: scrap metal is reclaimed, spare parts are sold and reused.

42. TEACH YOUR CHILDREN TO SAVE THE EARTH

BACKGROUND. If only our parents and our parents' parents had instilled a sense of the importance of the environment in their children, then perhaps some of the problems that we and our children now face would not be so urgent and pronounced.

For this planet to survive, we have to set a good example to the next generation through our own action and instruction.

DID YOU KNOW

● Kids Against Pollution, is a new pressure group in America that lobbies big corporations about their environmental record. Their main targets are companies that rely on children for a large proportion of their market. The kids therefore know that they will have to listen.

SIMPLE THINGS TO DO

● Encourage your children to put into practice at school what they have learned at home. It may need some liaison with their teachers, but there is no reason why kids should not start up their own paper, bottle and can recycling programmes at school.

● Teach them to precycle. Children are particularly susceptible to loud, colourful packaging, especially on products that they have seen on television. But children are quick learners, and have a special fondness of nature and wildlife. Teach them that they can help save the earth by using one kind of product instead of another, and by caring for their toys so they will not need replacing.

Writing to the Secretary of State for the Environment? The address is on p92.

- Buy toys that will last, and when your children outgrow them, pass them on. There are a number of toy libraries around the country that welcome donations, or you could give them to a local playgroup.

- Remember that children love to be creative with items like toilet rolls, egg cartons, yoghurt pots and magazines. Recycle them after the kids have finished with them.

- If your kids are particularly interested in conservation and the environment, you may consider involving them in a nature-orientated organisation. Here are some suggestions of groups that provide a range of activities for children:

Earth Action, c/o Friends of the Earth, 26–28 Underwood Street, London N1 7JQ

Watch, 22 The Green, Nettleham, Lincoln LN2 2NR

Young People's Trust for Endangered Species, 19 Quarry Street, Guildford, Surrey GU1 3EH

The world's shipping industry dumps over 450,000 plastic containers into the sea every day.

FOR THE

COMMITTED

43. START COMPOSTING

BACKGROUND. Composting is the process of turning organic material you normally throw away – from grass cuttings to apple cores – into rich fertiliser.

This does not mean you throw fresh kitchen garbage directly onto the soil. You put your organic garbage into a specially constructed receptacle, and then you have to maintain it.

How does it work? In a compost heap, billions of organisms break the organic wastes down into a form that can be best used by plants. The finished compost will add nutrients and humus to the soil, improving its texture and increasing its ability to hold air and water.

Besides being a source of natural fertiliser, composting helps cut down the amount of solid waste being dumped in crowded landfills.

DID YOU KNOW

● Around 30 percent of domestic refuse is organic material – Britain produces 9 million tonnes of it a year.

● Egg shells, tea leaves, fish-leftovers, vegetable peelings, and grass cuttings are all useful additions to the compost heap.

● The town of Davis, California, has been able, through composting and recycling, to cut its garbage in half.

SIMPLE THINGS TO DO

Start your own compost heap. The simplest way is to pile leaves, grass cuttings and weeds in a corner of your garden. This is not ideal as composting goes, and it takes up a lot of room, but the cuttings will decompose and will not use landfill space.

A more sophisticated compost pile involves more effort. You will need to:

● Sort your garbage to separate the organics from the rest – a bucket by the sink is probably easiest.

● Build or buy a small enclosure in which to create the compost.

Britain produces around 700,000 tonnes of newspaper per year.

- Learn how to stack and layer the compost.
- Turn it occasionally to avoid odours and allow the air to circulate.

It is a lot simpler than it might sound. For more information, contact the Henry Doubleday Research Association, National Centre for Organic Gardening, Ryton-on-Dunsmore, Coventry CV8 3LG.

If you do not have a garden:

- Composting is still worthwhile. Donate your compost to friends who garden.
- In the US, if you want to recycle your organic garbage without bothering to keep a compost heap, you can participate in a community composting project. We have found no record of this happening in Britain, but that is no reason for you not to start one now.

To produce one steak, 2,607 gallons of water are needed.

44. DRIVE LESS

BACKGROUND. Driving your car is probably the single most damaging contribution you make to the environment. We must all attempt to cut down on the amount of driving we do.

DID YOU KNOW

● In 1987, 29 percent of the UK's energy was consumed by transport.

● By 1985, 90 percent of passenger miles in Britain were travelled by road.

● A bike uses up little space, releases no pollution and provides healthy exercise.

● The car uses up 50 times more energy in its production than it will in its lifetime.

● If only 1 percent of the car owners in America left their cars idle for one day a week, it would save an estimated 35 million gallons of petrol a year. Destructive emissions would be reduced accordingly – around 840 million pounds of carbon dioxide would be kept out of the atmosphere.

SIMPLE THINGS TO DO

● The average number of miles travelled to and from work by car commuters is only 37 miles per week. This means that the typical car journey to work is less than 4 miles. If you make regular short journeys by car, consider the alternatives. Try using another means of transport just one day a week. Buses, trains, bicycles, the underground, or walking: even that may be difficult, but it is worth the effort.

IT CAN BE DONE
Other societies have managed to cut down:

● In the Netherlands 80 percent of train commuters get to the station by bicycle.

● In Denmark about 30 percent of all trips are taken on bikes.

● Japan has bicycle parking garages in urban areas.

It takes 100 times more water to produce a pound of meat than a pound of wheat.

45. CUT DOWN ON MEAT

BACKGROUND. We do not think that anyone should tell you what to eat, but you should know some of the facts about how your diet affects the environment. Many people never consider the resources that it takes to put a steak, for example, on their plate. For a long time, we have been blessed with a plentiful supply of food. Perhaps it is time we tried to conserve it.

DID YOU KNOW
● 100,000 square kilometres – an area the size of Austria – in Brazil, and half the forests of Central America, have been cleared for beef production.

● Over half the grain grown in the UK, and about 80 percent of our agricultural land is used for livestock.

● It has been estimated that if Americans reduced their meat intake by just 10 percent, the savings in grains and soybeans could adequately feed 60 million people – the number who starve to death, worldwide, each year.

● There are now over 4 million vegetarians in Britain.

● 61 pure vegetarians can be fed on the land needed to feed just one meat-eater.

● Research has revealed that vegetarians may live up to 9 years longer than people who eat meat.

SIMPLE THINGS TO DO
● The simplest thing, even if you are a confirmed meat-eater, is to cut down on the amount of meat you eat.

● Experiment with occasional vegetarian meals. There are lots of excellent vegetarian cookery books available.

● Try to grow produce in your garden. You may be surprised by how much you can grow in even a tiny plot. Herbs, vegetables and fruit can be grown easily in most urban settings.

The average Briton eats 330 lbs of meat a year.

46. START A RECYCLING PROGRAMME

BACKGROUND. By now you should be excited by recycling. But what happens if you discover that there is no recycling programme in your area? Set one up.

● If you are thinking about starting a plastic recycling programme in your area, contact the British Plastics Federation, 5 Belgrave Square, London SW1X 8PH. They will be delighted to help.

● You could earn money by organising a local aluminium collection scheme. For information, write to Alcan Enfield Alloys Ltd, Barnet Road, London Colney, St Albans, Hertfordshire AL2 1DN.

● Advice on voluntary collections of most items can be obtained from the National Anti-Waste Programme, Ashdown House, 123 Victoria Street, London SW1 6RB.

RECYCLING SUCCESS STORIES
Leeds
● In 1987/88, Leeds generated a surplus of £210,900 from saving over 4,000 tonnes of waste. The money was donated to charity.

Richmond
● In 1984 Richmond Borough became the first district council to appoint a recycling officer. They launched a campaign with the slogan 'Please don't choose what you can't reuse.' Richmond now recycles almost 10 percent of its waste.

In the summer, a layer of mulch around trees will slow the evaporation of moisture.

Sheffield

• In May 1989 Sheffield was launched as the first 'Recycling City'. This has involved a kerbside collection project, known as the Blue Box scheme. Households are issued with blue boxes for collecting cans, bottles, jars, plastic bottles, bags, newspapers, magazines and household batteries. These are emptied by specially designed vehicles once a week.

• It is the first time either plastic or household battery recycling facilities have been offered in the UK.

• A rebate from the council is received for every tonne of materials collected.

• The scheme is based on one already in operation in Ontario, Canada, which covers 1.5 million households and collects 18 percent of domestic waste for recycling, including over 50 percent of drinks' packaging. By 1992 Ontario hopes to have reduced waste that is landfilled by 25 percent, and by 50 percent in the year 2000.

• By 1991 a further three cities will have become involved in the national Recycling City project. The second will be Cardiff.

• Also in Sheffield, the Aluminium Can Recycling Association is offering target incentives such as bar magnets and hand operated crushers, as well as prizes for the highest per capita collection ratio.

In some American states it is now illegal for residents not to recycle.

47. ECOLOGY AWAY FROM HOME

BACKGROUND. When we go on holiday, we like to forget all about the everyday things that make up our lives at home and at work. But remember that being environmentally-minded is something that you should never take a break from, whether you are on a trip abroad, a weekend away or a day out.

DID YOU KNOW
● Pedestrians, drivers and passengers drop about 1 million tonnes of litter per annum in this country.

SIMPLE THINGS TO DO
● Wherever you are, always respect the landscape. Never leave litter, do not damage the flora and fauna, and be mindful of fire.

● If you are going away for a break, why not consider a green holiday? By doing so you will not only learn more about the environment, but you will be helping the country's conservation effort, too. Here are a few ideas:

The British Trust for Conservation Volunteers organise working holidays throughout the UK. The work can vary from picking up litter to building stone walls. Ask for a brochure by writing to the BTCV at 36 St Mary's Street, Wallingford, Oxfordshire OX10 0EU.

If you are interested in organic farming, there is an organisation that can arrange a fascinating experience for you. Write to Working Weekends on Organic Farms, 19 Bradford Road, Lewes, Sussex.

Or, if you are an avid birdwatcher, how about an ornithological holiday? There are many bodies that plan such things, but with the Royal Society for the Protection of Birds, you are assured that profits are funnelled back into conservation projects. Their address is: RSPB Holidays, The Lodge, Sandy, Bedfordshire SG19 2DL.

Soft drinks and beer in Denmark cannot be sold in non-returnable bottles.

48. XERISCAPE

BACKGROUND. Xeriscape (from the Greek word Xeros, meaning dry) is a modern approach to gardening which does not rely on a regular supply of water.

DID YOU KNOW

● Your garden water sprinkler uses around 200 gallons per hour. The more you use it, the more likely it is that a country valley will have to be converted into a water reservoir.

● Drought-resistant plants are not just limited to cacti and succulents. They include hundreds of species of colourful flowers, flowering shrubs, vines and ground cover that provide beautiful alternatives to traditional landscapes. For instance, jasmine, wisteria, sweet alyssum and daffodil are all plants that require minimal amounts of water.

SIMPLE THINGS TO DO

● We are not suggesting that you go out into your garden, dig up your lawn, and replace it with cactus. We just want you to look at alternative gardening methods that will be beneficial to the environment. Some of the principles of Xeriscape are applicable to any garden design, like heavy mulching of planting beds and organic soil improvements to allow for better water absorption and retention.

● To find out more about low-water gardening, visit the Anglian Water 'drought garden' near Rutland Water, which was created by Geoff Hamilton and Tony Ford. It is open all the year round.

● For a list of the plants in the garden apply to Kate Godley, Anglian Water Services, North Street, Oundle, Peterborough PE8 4AS.

Growing wildflowers and herbs will provide food for beneficial insects.

49. STAY INVOLVED

BACKGROUND. Some activists are worried that books like this one will lull people into believing that doing a few positive things for the environment is enough.

It is not. As was stated at the beginning, our '50 Simple Things' are just a start. By making them simple and accessible, we are trying to make it easier to get involved.

Now it is up to you to stay involved.

There are many ways to do it. One is to work with existing organisations. Here is a list of a few that you may consider writing to for more information about what they are doing, or what you can do.

The Department of the Environment, 2 Marsham Street, London SW1P 3EB
British Glass, Northumberland Road, Sheffield S10 2UA
The Can Makers, 36 Grosvenor Gardens, London SW1W 0EB
Industry Council for Packaging and the Environment, Premier House, 10 Greycoat Place, London SW1P 1SB

Association for the Protection of Rural Scotland, 14a Napier Road, Edinburgh EH10 5AY
Council for the Protection of Rural England, Warwick House, 25 Buckingham Palace Road, London SW1W 0PP
Council for the Protection of Rural Wales, Ty Gwyn, 31 High Street, Welshpool, Powys SY21 7JP
Earth Watch, Harbour View, Bantree, Co. Cork, Republic of Ireland
Friends of the Earth, 26–28 Underwood Street, London N1 7JQ
Friends of the Earth Scotland, 72 Newhaven Road, Edinburgh EH6 5QG, Scotland
Gaia Foundation, 18 Well Walk, Hampstead, London NW3 1LD
Green Alliance, 60 Chandos Place, London WC2N 4HG

In 1984, black snow as acid as vinegar fell in Aviemore.

Greenpeace UK, 30–31 Islington Green, London N1 8BR
International Institute for Environment and Development, 3 Endsleigh Street, London WC1H 0DD
Marine Conservation Society, 4 Gloucester Road, Ross-on-Wye, Herefordshire HR9 5BU
Men of the Trees, Turners Hill Road, Crawley Down, Crawley, West Sussex RH10 4HL
National Society for Clean Air, 136 North Street, Brighton BN1 1RG
Neighbourhood Energy Action, Energy Projects Office, 2nd Floor, Sunlight Chambers, 2–4 Bigg Market, Newcastle-upon-Tyne NE1 1VW
Oxfam, Oxfam House, 274 Banbury Road, Oxford OX2 7DZ
Survival International, 310 Edgware Road, London W2 1DY
Tidy Britain Group, Bostel House, 37 West Street, Brighton BN1 2RE
Transport 2000, Walkden House, 10 Melton Street, London NW1 2EJ
Tree Council, Agricultural House, Knightsbridge, London SW1X 7NJ
The Vegetarian Society, Parkdale, Dunham Road, Altrincham, Cheshire WA14 4QG
Waste Watch, NCVO, 26 Bedford Square, London WC1B 3HU
Women's Environmental Network, 287 City Road, London EC1V 1LA.
World Wide Fund for Nature, Panda House, Weyside Park, Godalming GU7 1XR

'When the well is dry, we know the worth of water' – Poor Richard's Almanack

50. SPREAD THE WORD

N ow that you have invested time reading this book and experimenting with the projects in it, you are aware of some of the ways that one person can make a difference.

Here is another one. Pass the book on to other people, or pass on what you have learned.

The 1990s should be a very exciting time, with people joining together to protect the most important asset we have – our environment. But in a powerful way, the ability to make this happen begins with you. Friends and family who see that you take environmental problems – and your part in solving them – seriously will show respect, and curiosity. Then they will listen as you pass on your knowledge and commitment.

It has a cumulative effect. As you inspire them, they will inspire others. Our ability to have a positive impact will grow proportionately.

We owe it to ourselves and our children to do whatever we can.

WRITE TO US
If you've got some more ideas
about how to save the earth,
and you'd like to pass them on,
we'd like to hear them.
We'll pass them on, too.

Write to:
THE EARTH WORKS GROUP
Box 25
1400 Shattuck Avenue
Berkeley, CA 94709
United States of America

ACKNOWLEDGMENTS

The Earth Works Group would like to thank everyone who worked with us to make this book possible, including:

John Javna, Julie Bennett, Fritz Springmeyer, Phil Catalfo, Robin Dellabough, Jayne Walker, Moira A. Hughes, Chris Calwell, The NRDC, Michael Brunsfield, Rob Pawlack, The Ecology Center, Karina Lutz of *Home Energy* magazine, Kathleen Kennedy, Marc Ledbetter of the American Council for an Energy-Efficient Economy, Pamela Lichtman of the Center for Marine Conservation, Eric Lefcowitz, Jean Byrne, Environmental Action, Dean Roberts and Walter Bischoff of Greenleaf, Andy Sohn, Susan Fassberg, Joe Pryborowski, Dick Bunnell, Debra Lynn Dadd, Joe Makower, 5th St. Computer Services, Gene Brissie, Peter Beren, Jay Feldman of the National Coalition Against the Misuse of Pesticides, Larry Weingarten, The Massachusetts Audubon Society, Renew America, Worldwatch Institute, The Texas Water Development Board, P G & E, EBMUD, Frances Flanigan of thé Alliance for the Chesapeke Bay, Marine World Africa USA, The Environmental Defense Fund, Citizens for a Better Environment, Bio-Integral Resource Center, The San Francisco Recycling Program, The Aluminum Association, Recycling Committee of the American Paper Institute, Rich Block of the World Wildlife Fund, National Wildlife Federation, Sally Fenn, Stewart Boyle, Bernardette Vallely.

AMERICAN SOURCES

ORGANISATIONS
Natural Resources Defense Council, 40W. 20th St., New York, NY 10011
Tire Industry Safety Council, PO Box 1801, Washington, DC 20013
The American Council for an Energy-Efficient Economy, 1001 Connecticut Avenue NW, Suite 535, Washington, DC 20036
The Household Hazardous Waste Project, Box 87, 901 South National Ave., Springfield, MO 65804.
Center for Environmental Education, 1725 DeSales St. NW, Washington, DC20036
The Oceanic Society, 218 D St.SE, Washington, DC 20003
World Wildlife Fund, 1255 23rd St.NW, Washington, DC 20037
National Wildlife Federation, 1412 16th St.NW, Washington, DC 20036
Earth Island Institute Dolphin Project, 300 Broadway No 28, San Francisco, CA 94133
The Bio-Integral Resource Center, PO Box 7414, Berkeley, CA 94707
Massachusetts Audubon Society, Lincoln, MA 01173
Paper Recycling Committee, American Paper Institute, 260 Madison Ave., New York, NY 10016
Earth Care Paper Company, PO Box 3335, Madison, WI 53704
Glass Packaging Institute, 1801 K St.NW, Washington, DC 20006
The Aluminum Association, 900 19th St.NW, Washington, DC 20006
Conservatree, 10 Lombard St., San Francisco CA 94111
San Francisco Recycling Program, 271 City Hall, SF., CA 94102
The Rainforest Action Network, 301 Broadway, Suite A, San Francisco, CA 94133
TreePeople, 12601 Mulholland Dr., Beverley Hills, CA 90210
Worldwatch Institute, 1776 Massachusetts Ave. NW, Washington, DC 20036
American Forestry Association, Global Releaf Program, PO Box 2000, Washington, DC 20013
National Coalition Against the Misuse of Pesticides, 530 7th St.SE, Washington, DC 20003
Water Pollution Control Federation, 601 Wythe St, Alexandria, VA 22314–1994
Sierra Club, 730 Polk St., San Francisco, CA 94009

PUBLICATIONS
Home Energy magazine, 2124 Kittredge St., No 95, Berkeley, CA 94704
Gas Mileage Guide, Consumer Information Center, Pueblo, CO 81009
Making the Switch: Alternatives to Using Toxic Chemicals in the Home by the Local Government Commission, Sacramento, CA
Nontoxic and Natural, and *The Nontoxic Home* by Debra Lynn Dadd
Garbage magazine, PO Box 56519, Boulder, CO 80322
The Environmental Shopper by the Pennsylvania Resources Council, 25 West 3rd St., Media, PA 19063
Mothering magazine, PO Box 1690, Santa Fe, New Mexico 87504
Home Composting by the Seattle Tilth Association, 4649 Sunnyside Ave., No., Seattle, Washington 98103
Diet for a New America by John Robbins